C000319643

Non-Verbal Reasoning

The 11+
10-Minute Tests

For the CEM (Durham University) test

Ages
10-11

Practise • Prepare • Pass
Everything your child needs for 11+ success

How to use this book

This book is made up of 10-minute tests and puzzle pages.
There are answers and detailed explanations in the pull-out section at the back of the book.

10-Minute Tests

- There are 31 tests in this book, each containing 18 or 19 questions.

- Each test is designed to cover a good range of the question styles and topics that your child could come across in the non-verbal reasoning sections of their 11+ test, at the same difficulty level.

- Your child should aim to score at least 16 in each 10-minute test.
  If they score less than this, use their results to work out the areas they need more practice on.

- If your child hasn't managed to finish the test in time, they need to work on increasing their speed, whereas if they have made a lot of mistakes, they need to work more carefully.

- Keep track of your child's scores using the progress chart on the inside back cover of the book.

Puzzle Pages

- There are 10 puzzle pages in this book, which are a great break from test-style questions. They encourage children to practise the same skills that they will need in the test, but in a fun way.

Published by CGP

Editors:
Emily Garrett, Sharon Keeley-Holden, Rebecca Tate, Ben Train

With thanks to Alison Griffin and Glenn Rogers for the proofreading.

Please note that CGP is not associated with CEM or The University of Durham in any way.
This book does not include any official questions and it is not endorsed by CEM or The University of Durham.
CEM, Centre for Evaluation and Monitoring, Durham University and *The University of Durham*
are all trademarks of The University of Durham.

ISBN: 978 1 78294 260 3
Printed by Elanders Ltd, Newcastle upon Tyne
Clipart from Corel®

Based on the classic CGP style created by Richard Parsons.

Text, design, layout and original illustrations © Coordination Group Publications Ltd. (CGP) 2015
All rights reserved.

Photocopying this book is not permitted. Extra copies are available from CGP with next day delivery.
0800 1712 712 • www.cgpbooks.co.uk

Contents

Question Type Examples

These pages contain a completed example question for each question type that appears in this book. Have a look through them to familiarise yourself with the question types before you do the tests.

Odd One Out

Find the figure in each row that is most unlike the other figures.

Example:

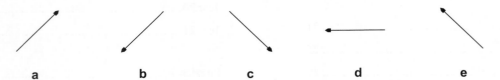

Answer: d

In all other figures, the arrow points diagonally.

Find the Figure Like the First Two or Three

Work out which option is most like the two or three figures on the left.

Example:

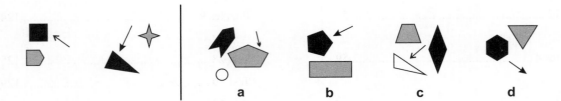

Answer: b

All figures must have an arrow pointing at a black shape.

Complete the Hexagonal Grid

Work out which of the options best fits in place of the missing hexagon in the grid.

Example:

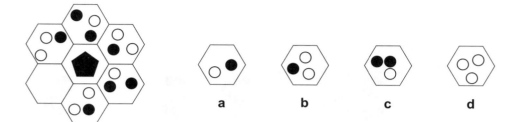

Answer: c

Going round the outer hexagons, the number of black circles alternates between one and two.

Complete the Square Grid

Work out which of the options best fits in place of the missing square in the grid.

Example:

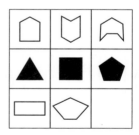

a   b   c   d

Answer: c

Working from left to right, the number of sides of the shape increases by one in each grid square.

Look at how the first two figures are changed, and then work out which option would look like the third figure if you changed it in the same way. (In some questions just one figure will change into another. This figure will look like a bug.)

Example:

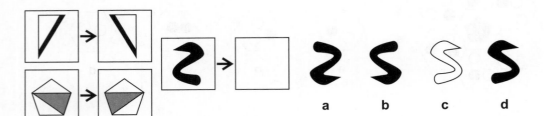

a   b   c   d

Answer: d

The figure reflects across.

Work out which of the options best fits in place of the missing square in the series. (Occasionally, the series might be made up of two pairs of squares. These questions are solved in a similar way to Complete the Pair questions.)

Example:

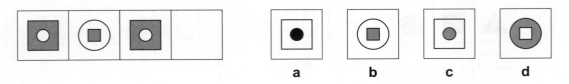

a   b   c   d

Answer: b

The figures alternate between a white circle in a grey square and a grey square in a white circle.

4

© CGP — not to be photocopied

Rotate the Figure

Work out which option would look like the figure on the left if it was rotated.

Example:

 Rotate

                        a   **b**   **c**   **d**

Answer: d

The figure has been rotated 90 degrees clockwise.

Reflect the Figure

Work out which option would look like the figure on the left if it was reflected over the line.

Example:

 Reflect

                        a   **b**   **c**   **d**

Answer: b

Options A and D are rotations of the shape on the left. Option C has not been reflected.

3D Rotation

Work out which 3D figure in the grey box has been rotated to make the new 3D figure.

Example:

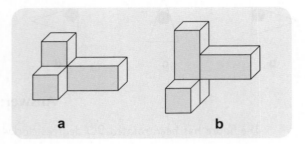

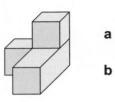

a

b

Answer: a

Figure A has been rotated 90 degrees right-to-left (see the glossary on page 142).

3D Building Blocks

Work out which set of blocks can be put together to make the 3D figure on the left.

Example:

 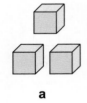

a   **b**   **c**   **d**

Answer: b

The block at the bottom of B rotates to become the block at the back of the figure. The two cubes move to the front.

Work out which option is a top-down 2D view of the 3D figure on the left.

Example:

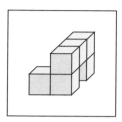 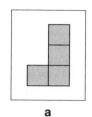 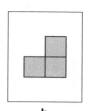 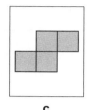 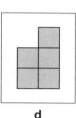

a   **b**   **c**   **d**

Answer: a

There are four blocks visible from above, which rules out options B and D.
There is a line of three blocks on the right-hand side of the shape, which rules out option C.

Cubes and Nets

Work out which of the four cubes can be made from the net.

Example:

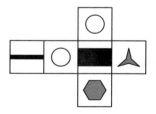

a   **b**   **c**   **d**

Answer: c

There is no black circle, which rules out option A. The thick black line and the thin black line must be on opposite sides, which rules out option B. There is only one grey hexagon, which rules out option D.

Test 1

You have **10 minutes** to do this test. Circle the letter for each correct answer.

Work out which of the options best fits in place of the missing hexagon in the grid.

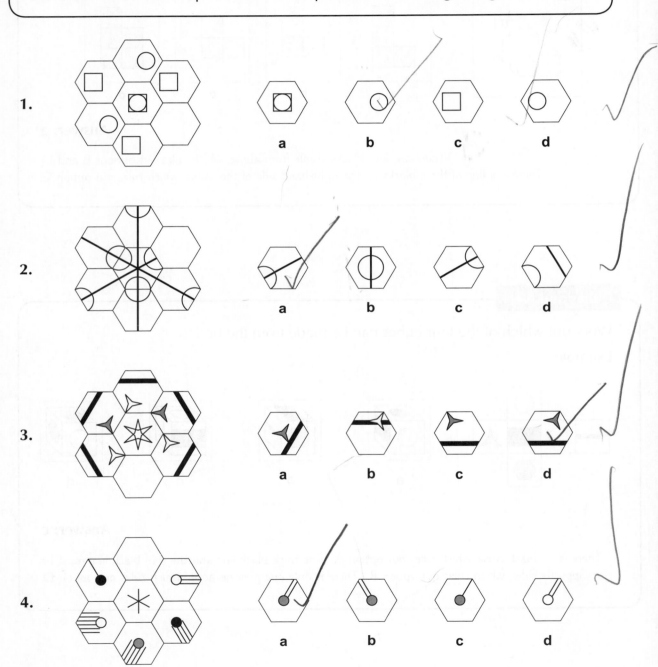

Test 1   8   © CGP — not to be photocopied

Work out which 3D figure in the grey box has been rotated to make the new 3D figure.

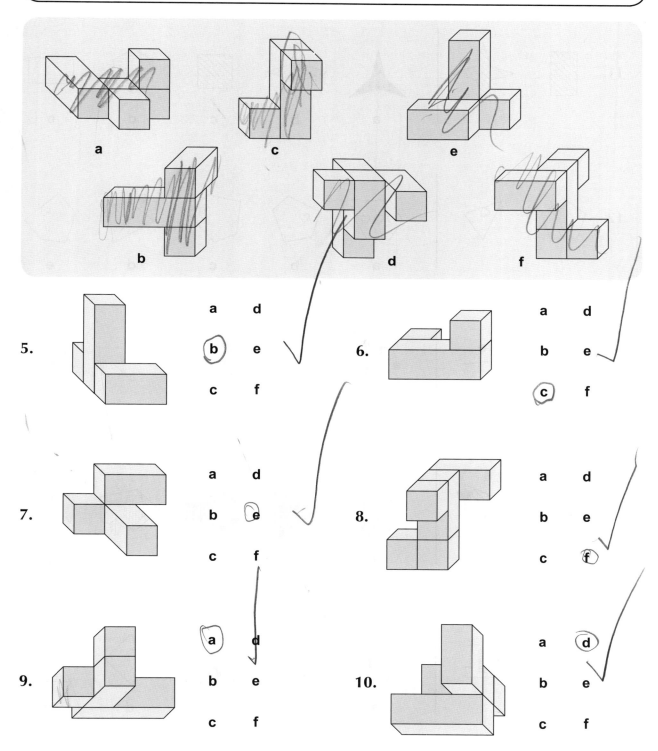

a

c

e

b

d

f

5.

a   d

(b)   e

c   f

6.

a   d

b   e

(c)   f

7.

a   d

b   (e)

c   f

8.

a   d

b   e

c   (f)

9.

(a)   d

b   e

c   f

10.

a   (d)

b   e

c   f

© CGP — not to be photocopied

9

Work out which option is most like the two figures on the left.

11.   a   b   c   d   e

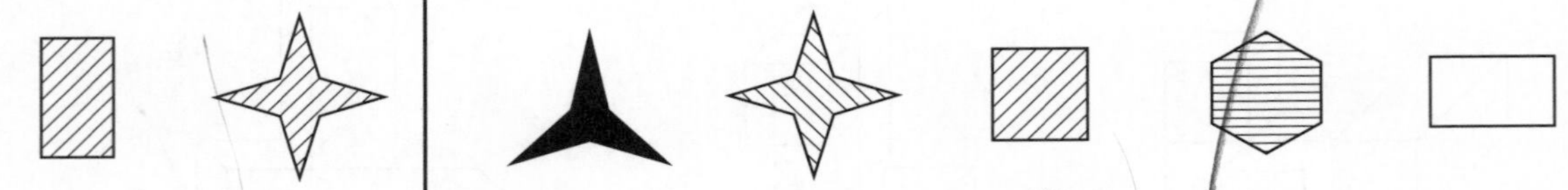

12.   a   b   c   d   e

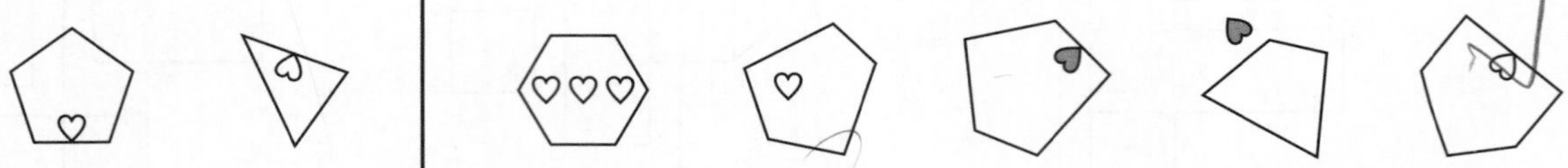

13.   a   b   c   d   e

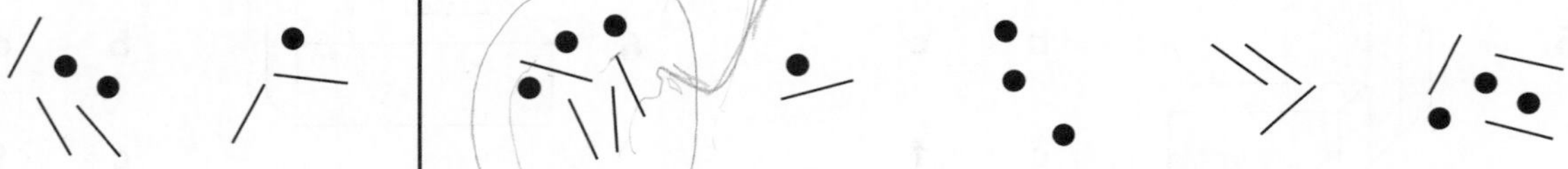

14.   a   b   c   d   e

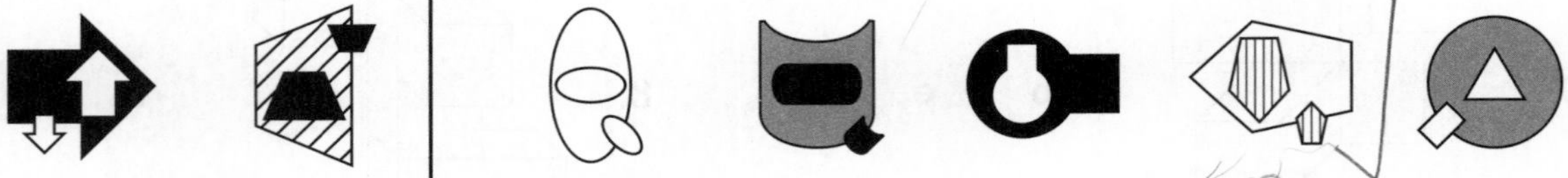

15.   a   b   c   d   e

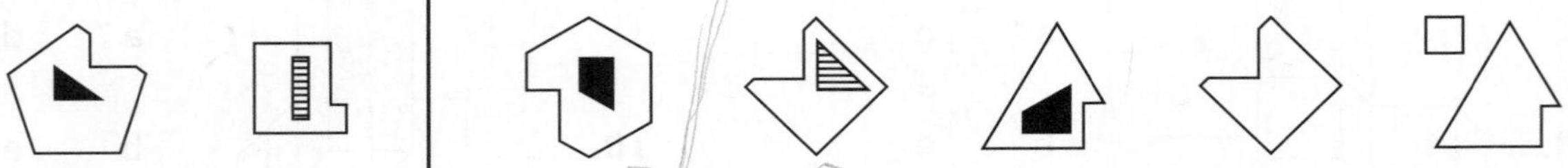

Look at how the first two figures are changed, and then work out which option would look like the third figure if you changed it in the same way.

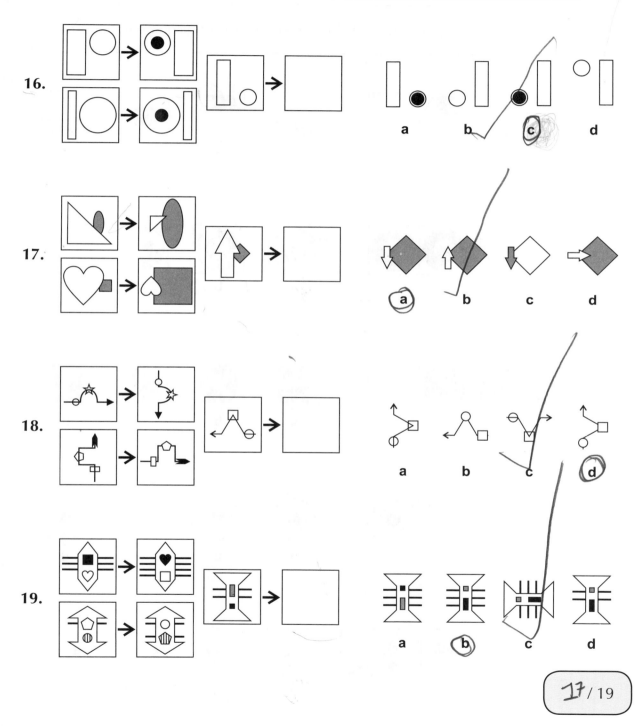

16.

a   b   c   d

17.

a   b   c   d

18.

a   b   c   d

19.

a   b   c   d

17 / 19

© CGP — not to be photocopied

11

Test 1

Test 2

You have **10 minutes** to do this test. Circle the letter for each correct answer.

Work out which of the options best fits in place of the missing square in the series.

1. 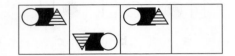
                                                    a   b   c   d

2. 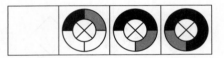
                                                    a   b   c   d

3. 
                                                    a   b   c   d

4. 
                                                    a   b   c   d

5. 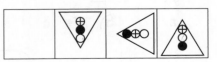
                                                    a   b   c   d

 © CGP — not to be photocopied

Work out which option would look like the figure on the left if it was rotated.

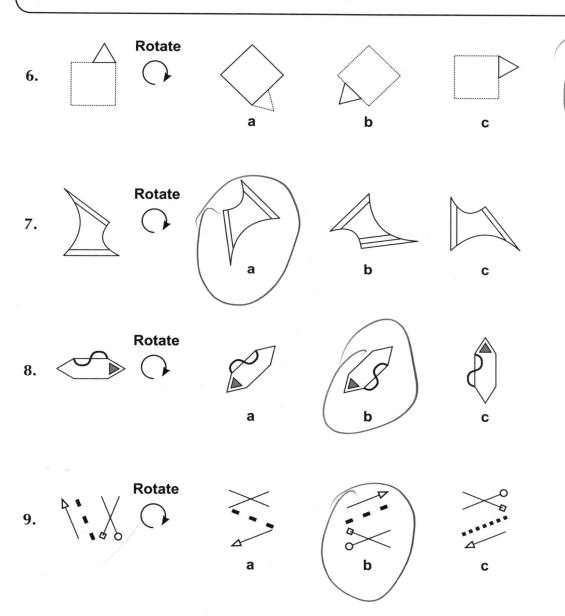

6. **Rotate**   a   b   c   d

7. **Rotate**   a   b   c   d

8. **Rotate**   a   b   c   d

9. **Rotate**   a   b   c   d

10. **Rotate**   a   b   c   d

© CGP — not to be photocopied

Test 2

Find the figure in each row that is most unlike the others.

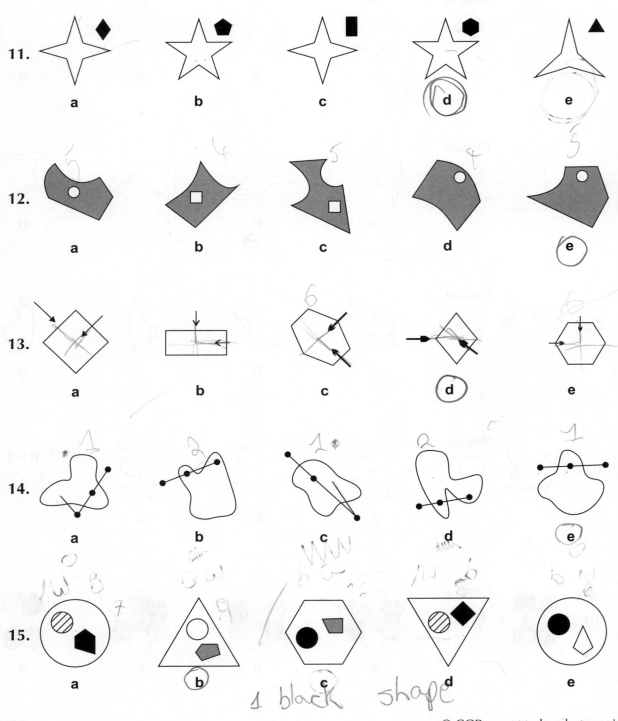

11.   a   b   c   d   e

12.   a   b   c   d   e

13.   a   b   c   d   e

14.   a   b   c   d   e

15.   a   b   c   d   e

1 black shape

Work out which of the four cubes can be made from the net.

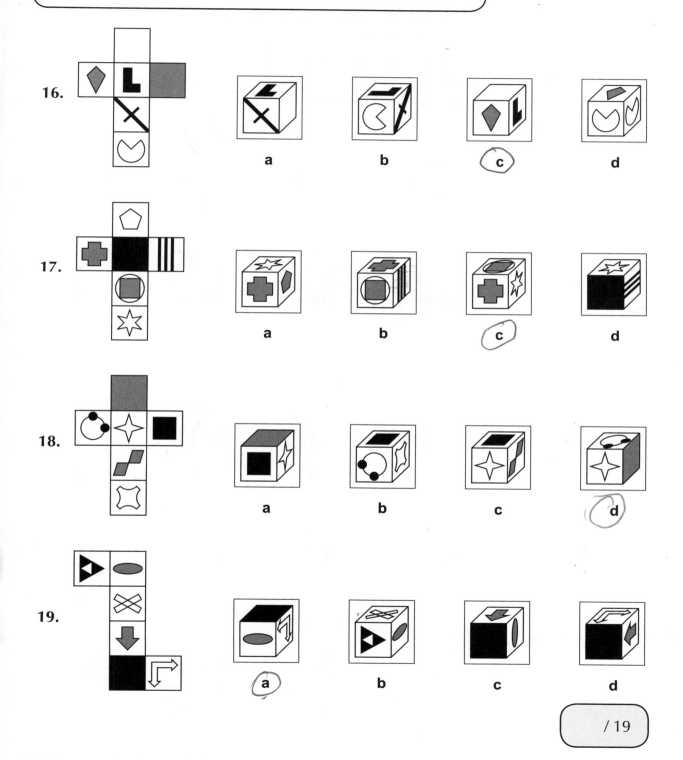

16.

a   b   c   d

17.

a   b   c   d

18.

a   b   c   d

19.

a   b   c   d

/ 19

© CGP — not to be photocopied

15

Test 3

You have **10 minutes** to do this test. Circle the letter for each correct answer.

Work out which option would look like the figure on the left if it was reflected over the line.

Reflect

1.
a   b   c   d

Reflect

2.
a   b   c   d

Reflect

3.
a   b   c   d

Reflect

4.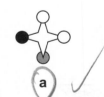
a   b   c   d

Reflect

5.
a   b   c   d

Test 3

16

© CGP — not to be photocopied

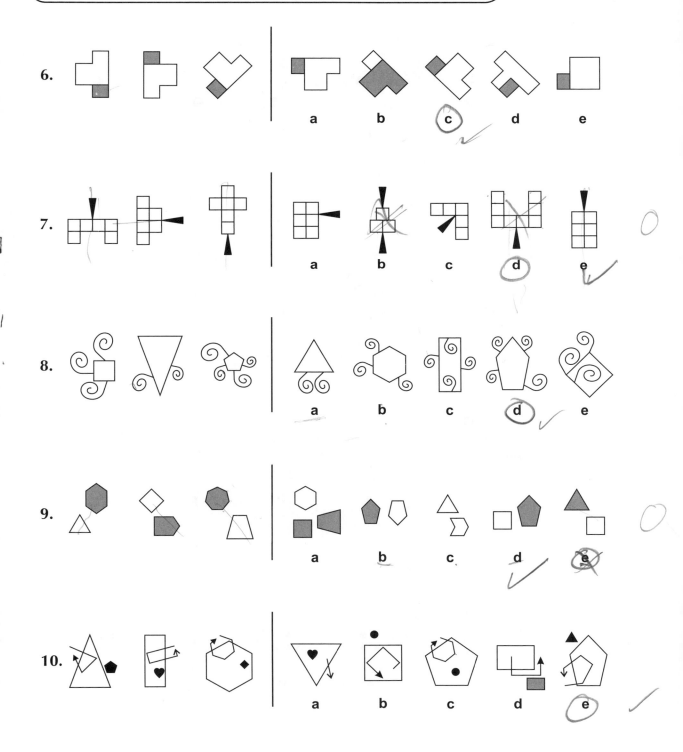

6.

a   b   c   d   e

7.

a   b   c   d   e

8.

a   b   c   d   e

9.

a   b   c   d   e

10.

a   b   c   d   e

Work out which of the options best fits in place of the missing hexagon in the grid.

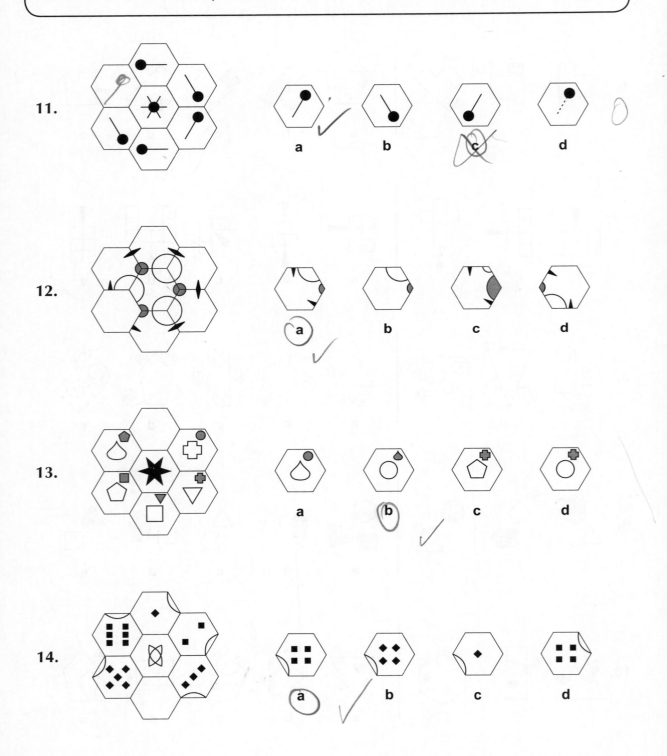

11.   a ✓   b   c   d

12.   a ✓   b   c   d

13.   a   b ✓   c   d

14.   a ✓   b   c   d

Look at how the first two figures are changed, and then work out which option would look like the third figure if you changed it in the same way.

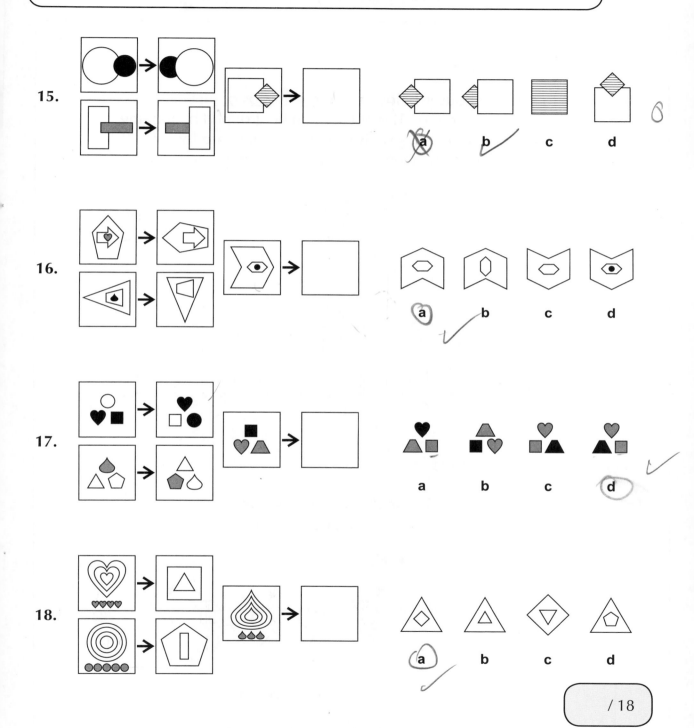

15.

16.

17.

18.

/ 18

Time for a break! These puzzles are a great way to practise **spotting similarities**.

Happy Houses

Draw lines to split the houses below into <u>three groups of three</u> — two lines have been drawn for you. The houses can be grouped by looking at just one feature of all the houses. Be careful — there are lots of similarities and differences between the houses, but only one solution.

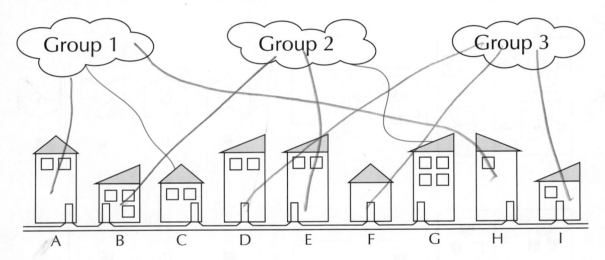

What's the Word?

For each of the top figures, choose the figure most similar to it and circle the letter underneath to spell out a word.

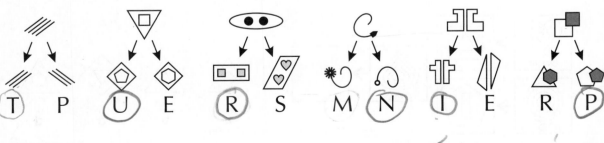

The word is: Turnip

20
© CGP — not to be photocopied

Test 4

You have **10 minutes** to do this test. Circle the letter for each correct answer.

Work out which option would look like the figure on the left if it was rotated.

1. **Rotate**

                       a   b   c   d

2. **Rotate**   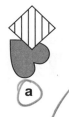

                       a   b   c   d

3. **Rotate**

                       a   b   c   d

4.  **Rotate**   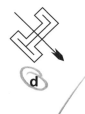

                       a   b   c   d

5. **Rotate**   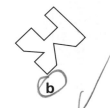

                       a   b   c   d

© CGP — not to be photocopied   21   Test 4

Work out which of the four cubes can be made from the net.

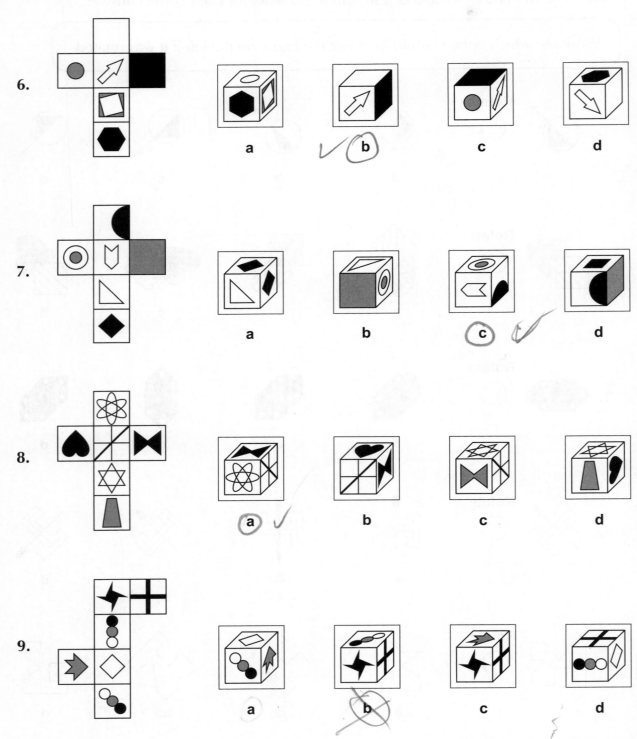

6.

a b ✓ c d

7.

a b c ✓ d

8.

a ✓ b c d

9.

a b ✗ c d

Look at how the first bug changes to become the second bug. Then work out which option would look like the third bug if you changed it in the same way.

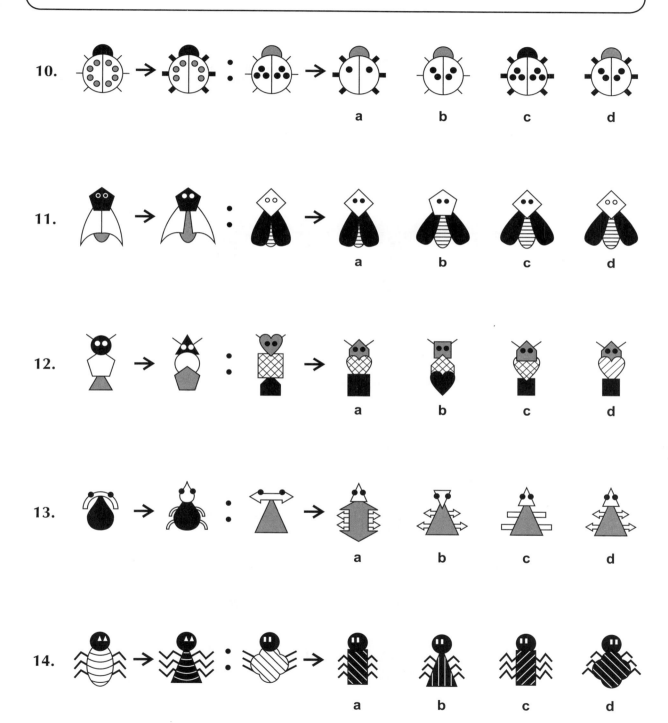

10.

11.

12.

13.

14.

a   b   c   d

© CGP — not to be photocopied
23

Work out which of the options best fits in place of the missing square in the grid.

15.

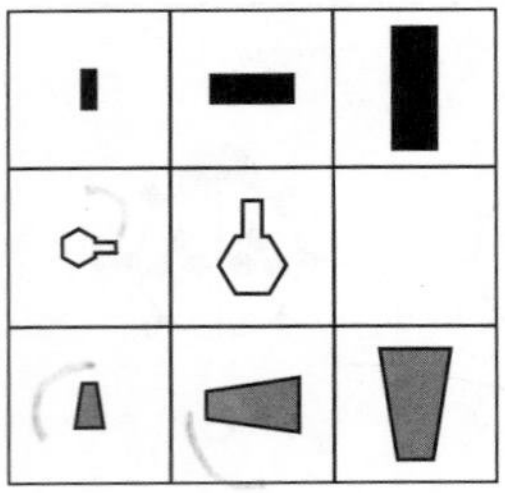

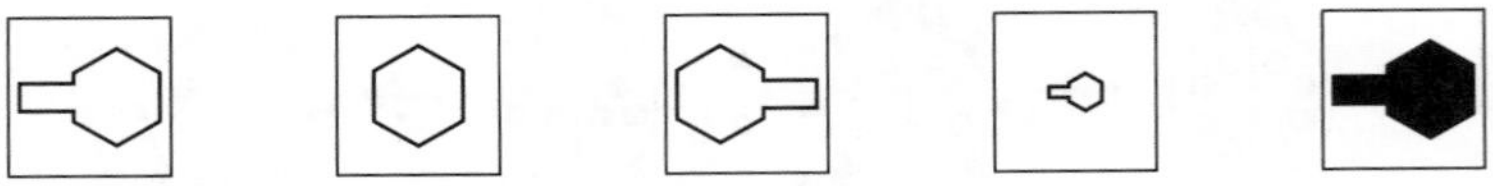

a b c d e

16.

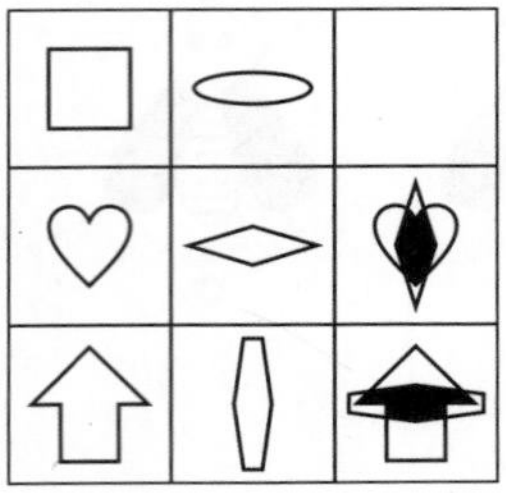

a b c d e

17.

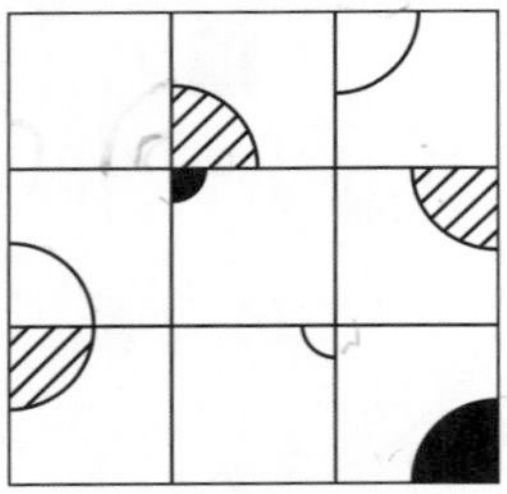

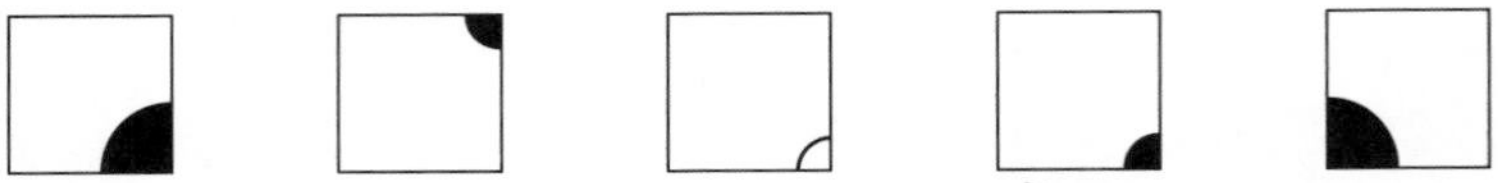

a b c d e

18.

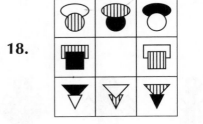

a b c d e

/ 18

© CGP — not to be photocopied

You have **10 minutes** to do this test. Circle the letter for each correct answer.

Work out which 3D figure in the grey box has been rotated to make the new 3D figure.

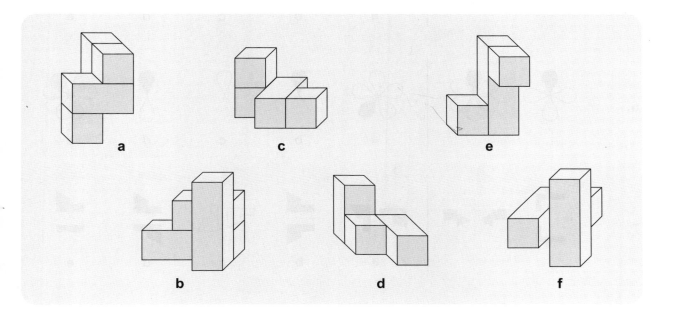

a

c

e

b

d

f

1.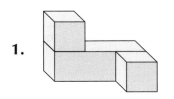

a   d

b   (e)

c   f

2.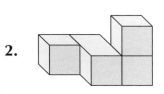

a   d

b   e

(c)   f ✓

3.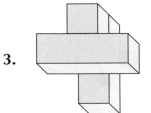

a   d

b   e

c   (f) ✓

4.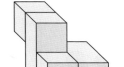

(a)   d ✓

b   e

c   f

Work out which option is most like the two figures on the left.

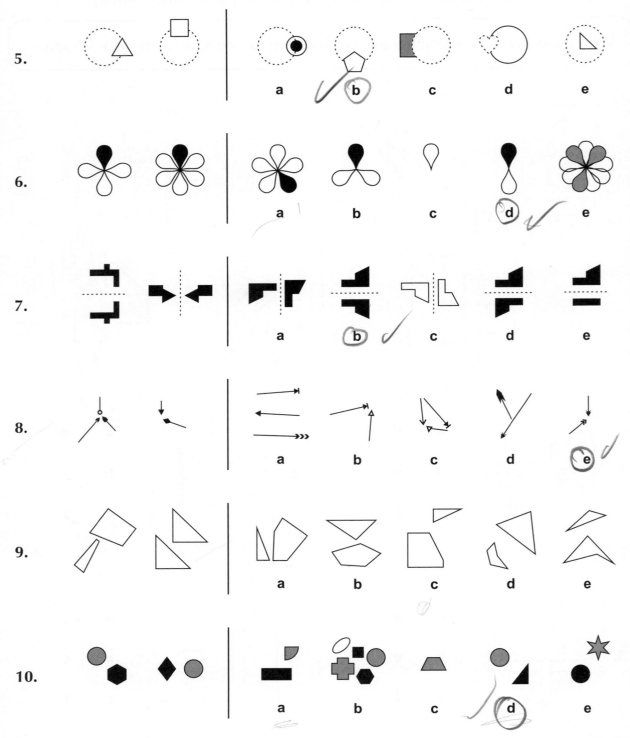

5.
          a   b   c   d   e

6.
          a   b   c   d   e

7.
          a   b   c   d   e

8.
          a   b   c   d   e

9.
          a   b   c   d   e

10.
          a   b   c   d   e

        © CGP — not to be photocopied

Work out which option would look like the figure on the left if it was reflected over the line.

Reflect

11.

a   b   c   d

Reflect

12.

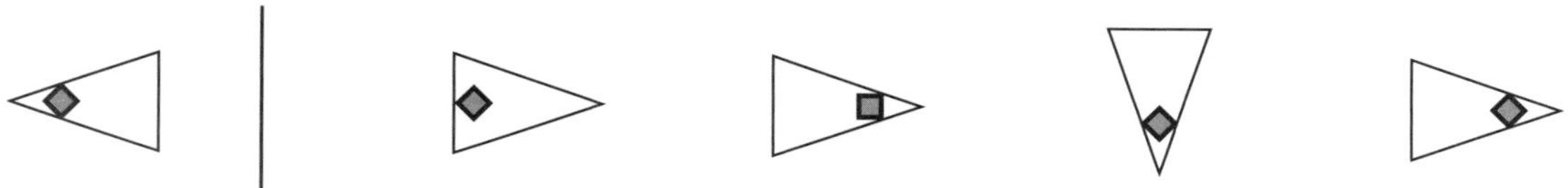

a   b   c   d

Reflect

13.

a   b   c   d

Reflect

14.

a   b   c   d

Reflect

15.

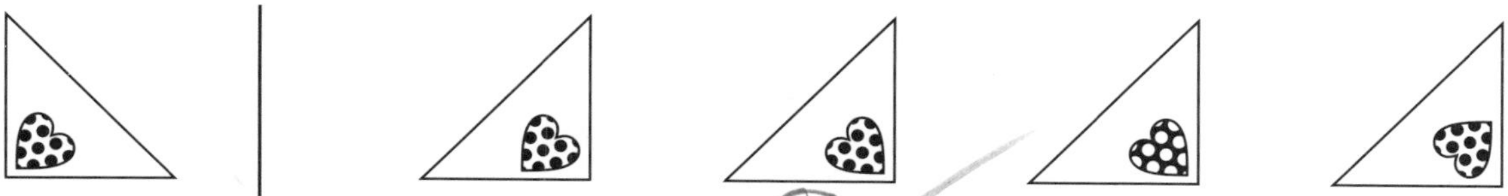

a   b   c   d

Work out which of the options best fits in place of the missing square in the grid.

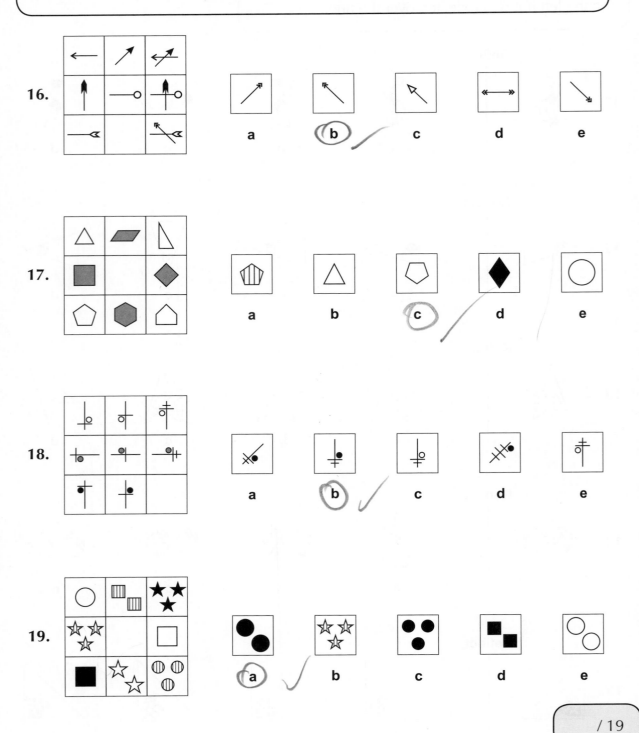

16.

a b c d e

17.

a b c d e

18.

a b c d e

19.

a b c d e

/ 19

28   © CGP — not to be photocopied

⏱ 10

You have **10 minutes** to do this test. Circle the letter for each correct answer.

Find the figure in each row that is most unlike the others.

1.

   a   b   c   d   e

2.

   a   b   c   d   e

3.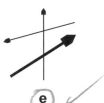

   a   b   c   d   e

4.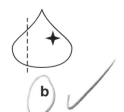

   a   b   c   d   e

5.

   a   b   c   d   e

© CGP — not to be photocopied   29   Test 6

Work out which option would look like the figure on the left if it was rotated.

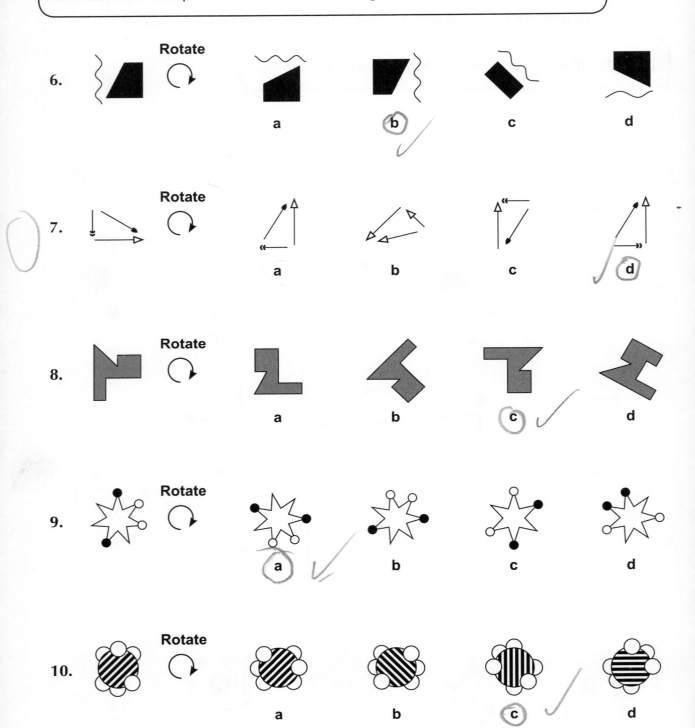

6. **Rotate**

a   b ✓   c   d

7. **Rotate**

a   b   c   d ✓

8. **Rotate**

a   b   c ✓   d

9. **Rotate**

a ✓   b   c   d

10. **Rotate**

a   b   c ✓   d

Work out which option is a top-down 2D view of the 3D figure on the left.

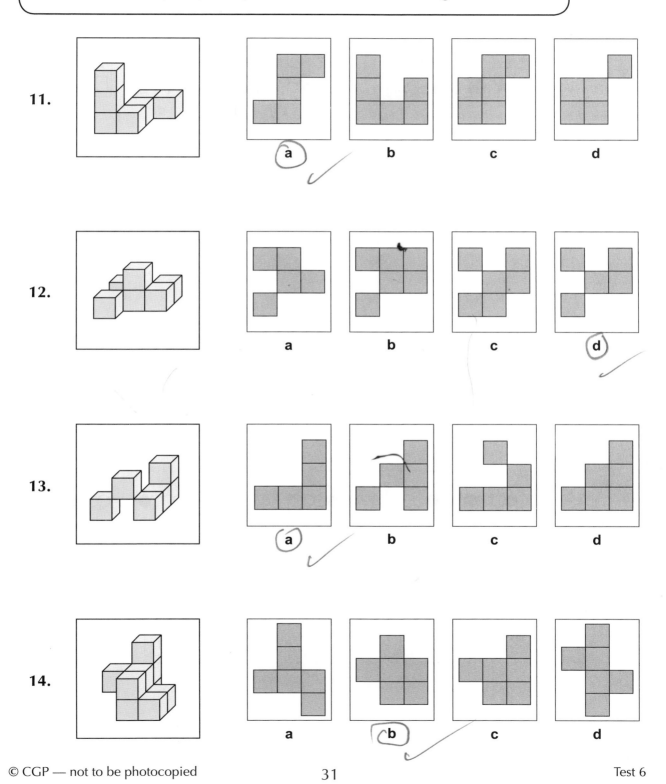

11.

a ✓ b c d

12.

a b c d ✓

13.

a ✓ b c d

14.

a b ✓ c d

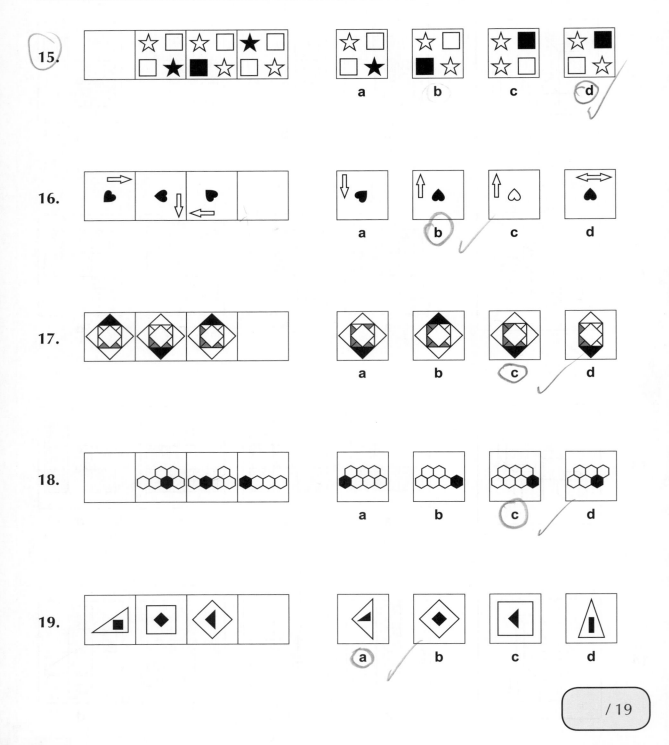

15.

16.

17.

18.

19.

/ 19

© CGP — not to be photocopied

Puzzles 2

These puzzles will help you practise skills you'll need in the test — so get cracking.

Secret Squares

Place the shapes ♡, ●, ■ and △ in the grids below so that every row and column contains each shape exactly once.

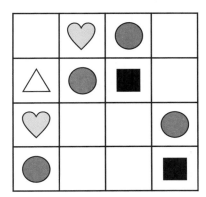 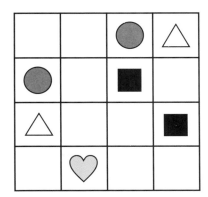

Mystery Number

Some of the squares below can be arranged into a sequence. The sequence will reveal a mystery six-digit number. The first two digits in the number are 1 and 6 — use these squares to work out what the sequence is. Then follow the sequence to find the rest of the mystery number.

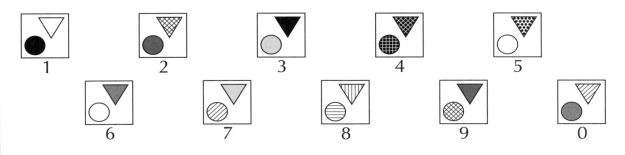

Mystery number: <u>1</u> <u>6</u> __ __ __ __

© CGP — not to be photocopied

Test 7

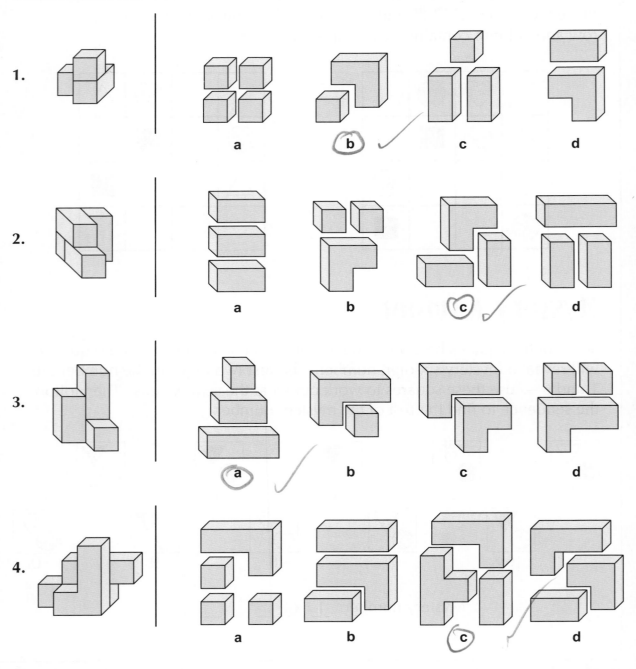

You have **10 minutes** to do this test. Circle the letter for each correct answer.

Work out which set of blocks can be put together to make the 3D figure on the left.

© CGP — not to be photocopied

Work out which of the options best fits in place of the missing hexagon in the grid.

5.

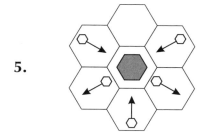

a

b

c   d

6.

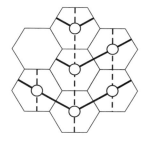

a

b

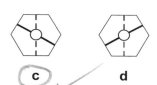

c   d

7.

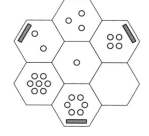

a   b

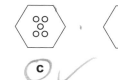

c   d

8.

a

b

c

d

© CGP — not to be photocopied

Test 7

Work out which of the options best fits in place of the missing square in the series.

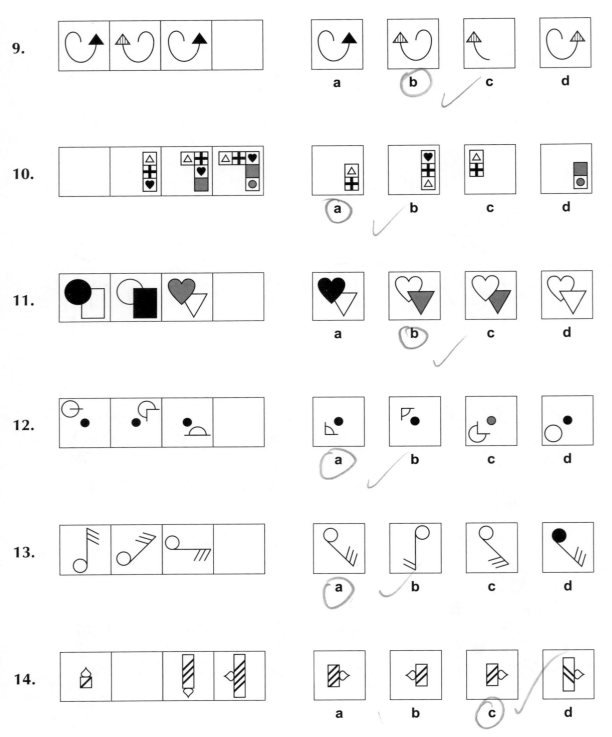

9.

10.

11.

12.

13.

14.

36

© CGP — not to be photocopied

Work out which option is most like the three figures on the left.

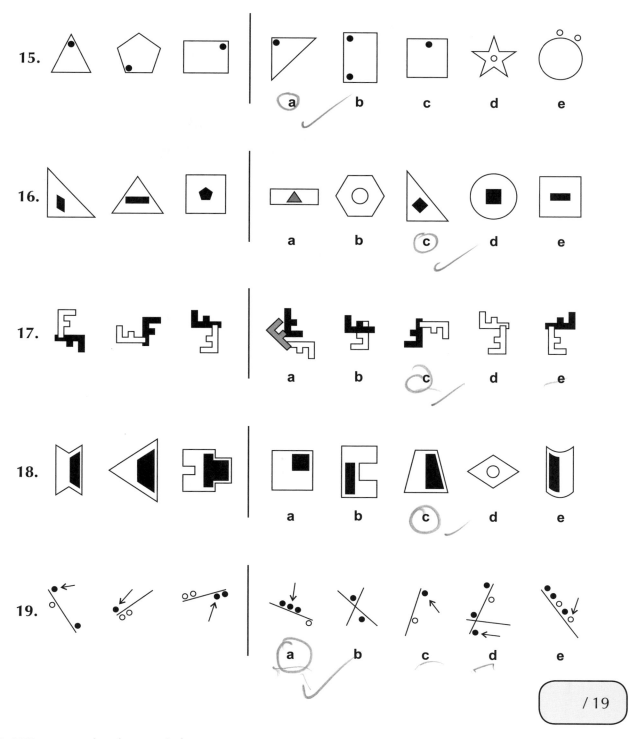

15. a ✓

16. c

17. c

18. c

19. a ✓

/ 19

You have **10 minutes** to do this test. Circle the letter for each correct answer.

> Find the figure in each row that is most unlike the others.

1.
  a   b   c   d   e

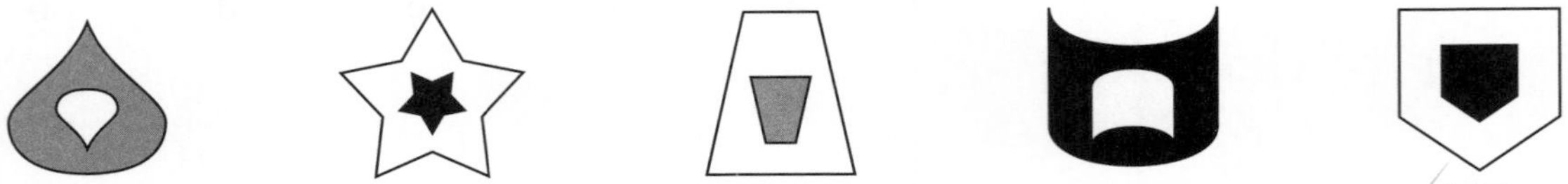

2.
  a   b   c   d   e

3.
  a   b   c   d   e

4.
  a   b   c   d   e

5.
  a   b   c   d   e

Work out which of the options best fits in place of the missing square in the grid.

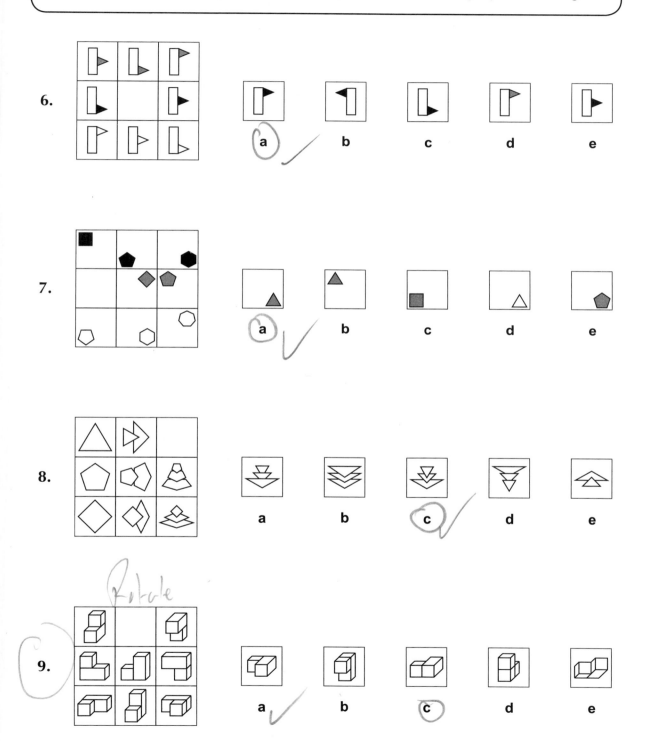

6.

a

b

c

d

e

7.

a

b

c

d

e

8.

a

b

c

d

e

9.

a

b

c

d

e

© CGP — not to be photocopied

39

Test 8

Work out which option would look like the figure on the left if it was reflected over the line.

Reflect

10.
   a   b   c   d 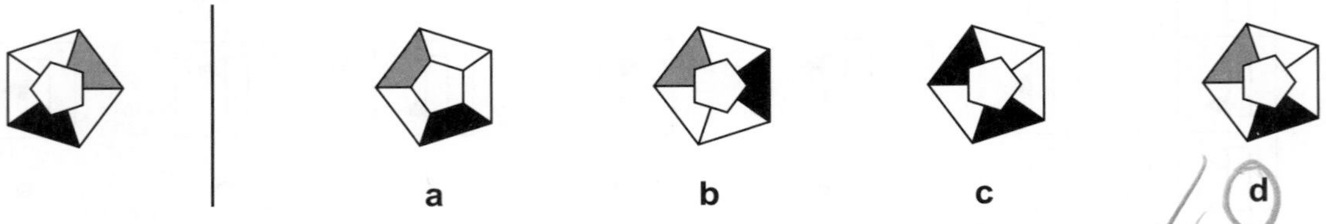

11.
   a   b   c   d 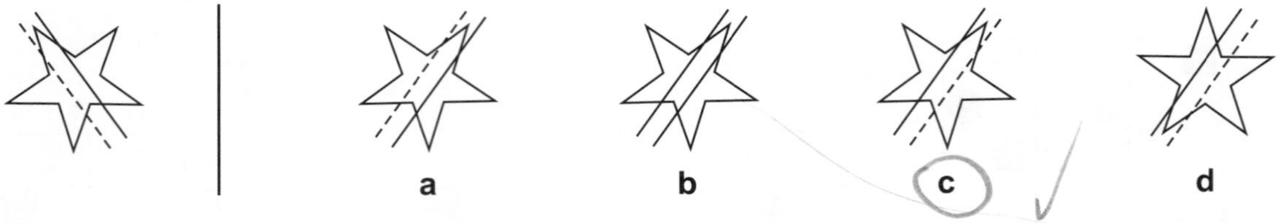

12.
   a   b   c   d 

13.
   a   b   c   d 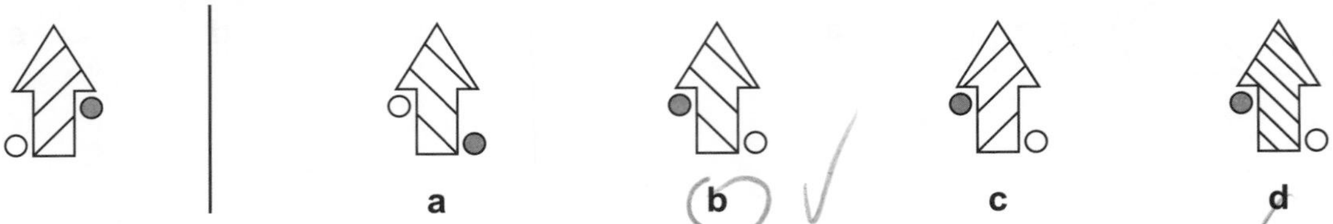

14.
   a   b   c   d

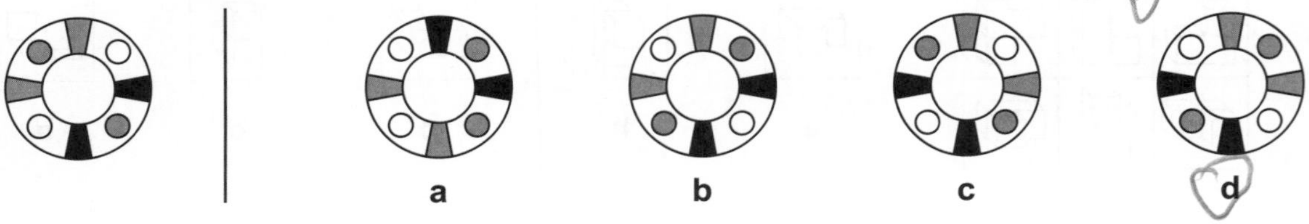

Work out which 3D figure in the grey box has been rotated to make the new 3D figure.

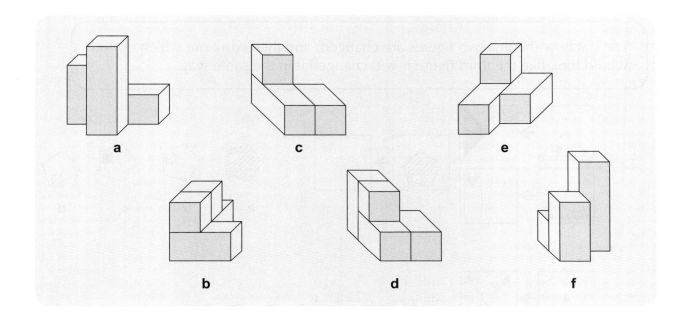

a

c

e

b

d

f

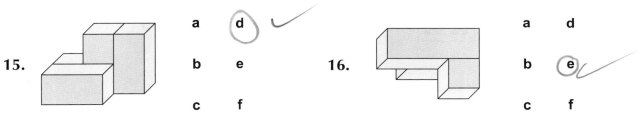

15.

a   (d) ✓

b   e

c   f

16.

a   d

b   (e) ✓

c   f

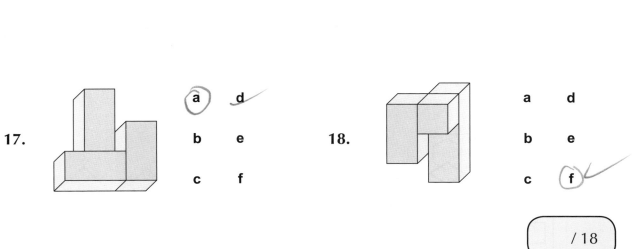

17.

(a)   d ✓

b   e

c   f

18.

a   d

b   e

c   (f) ✓

/ 18

© CGP — not to be photocopied

41

You have **10 minutes** to do this test. Circle the letter for each correct answer.

Look at how the first two figures are changed, and then work out which option would look like the third figure if you changed it in the same way.

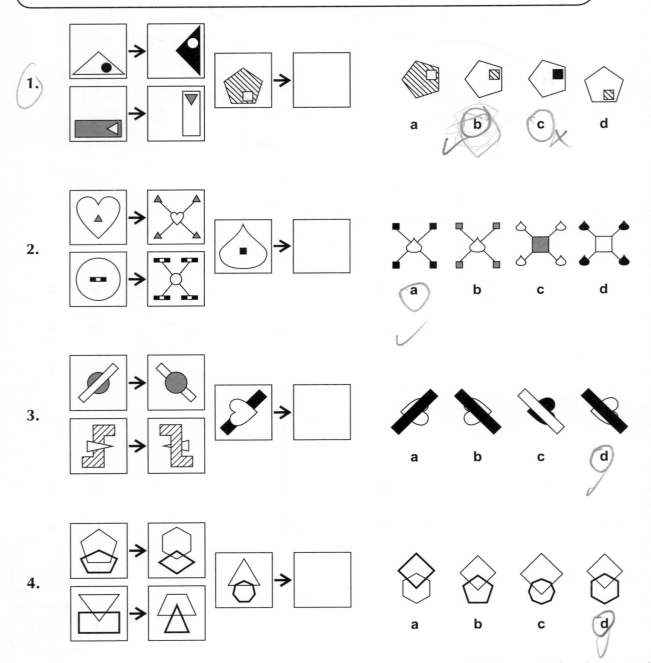

42
© CGP — not to be photocopied

Work out which of the options best fits in place of the missing square in the series.

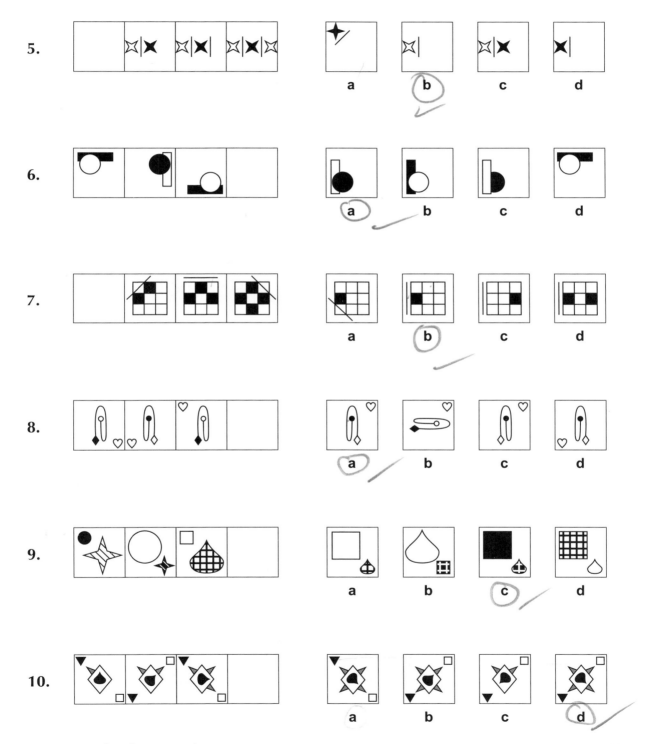

5.

a   b   c   d

6.

a   b   c   d

7.

a   b   c   d

8.

a   b   c   d

9.

a   b   c   d

10.

a   b   c   d

© CGP — not to be photocopied

43

Test 9

Work out which of the four cubes can be made from the net.

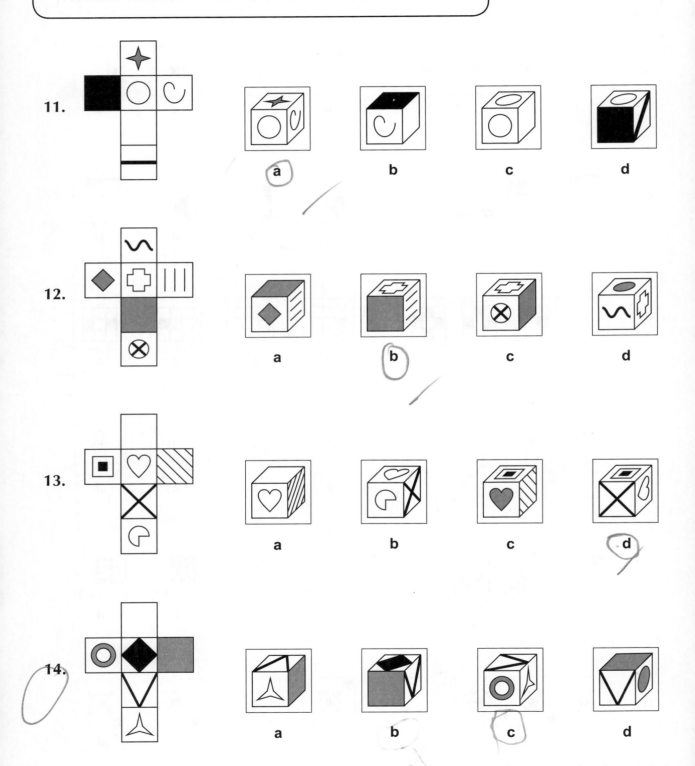

11.

a   b   c   d

12.

a   b   c   d

13.

a   b   c   d

14.

a   b   c   d

44

© CGP — not to be photocopied

Work out which option would look like the figure on the left if it was reflected over the line.

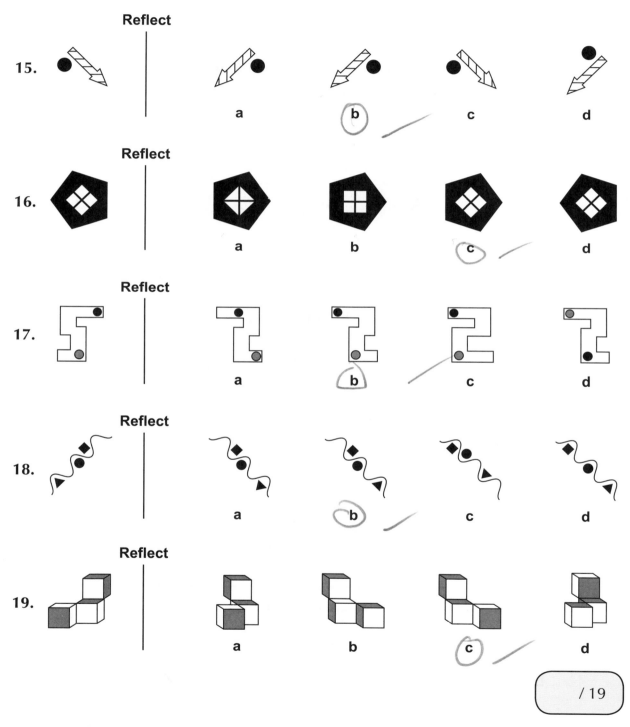

Reflect

15.

   a   b   c   d

Reflect

16.

   a   b   c   d

Reflect

17.

   a   b   c   d

Reflect

18.

   a   b   c   d

Reflect

19.

   a   b   c   d

/ 19

© CGP — not to be photocopied

Test 9

Puzzles 3

It's puzzle time! This page will help you practise your **2D** and **3D shape** skills.

Hidden Shape

The shape on the left is hidden in two of the squares on the right.
Circle the letters with the hidden shape.

                        A   B   C   D   E

Mental Block

The shape below has been made from blocks, but some joins between the blocks have been covered up.

Work out which set of blocks could **<u>not</u>** have been used to make the shape.

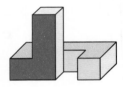

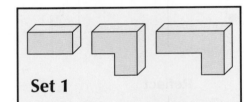

Set 1

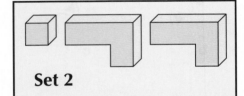

Set 2

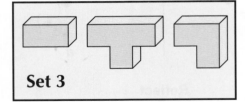

Set 3

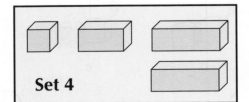

Set 4

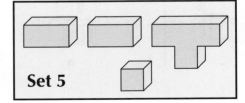

Set 5

 © CGP — not to be photocopied

You have **10 minutes** to do this test. Circle the letter for each correct answer.

Work out which of the options best fits in place of the missing square in the grid.

1.

a   **b** ✓   c   d   e

2.

a   **b** ✓   c   d   e

3.

a ✓   b   c   d   e

4.

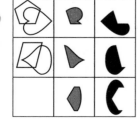

a   **b** ✓   c   d   e

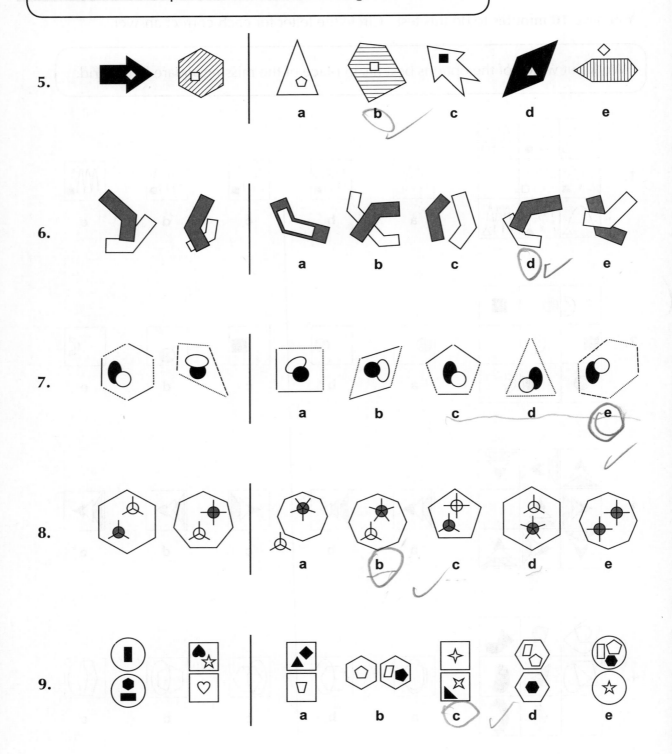

5.

6.

7.

8.

9.

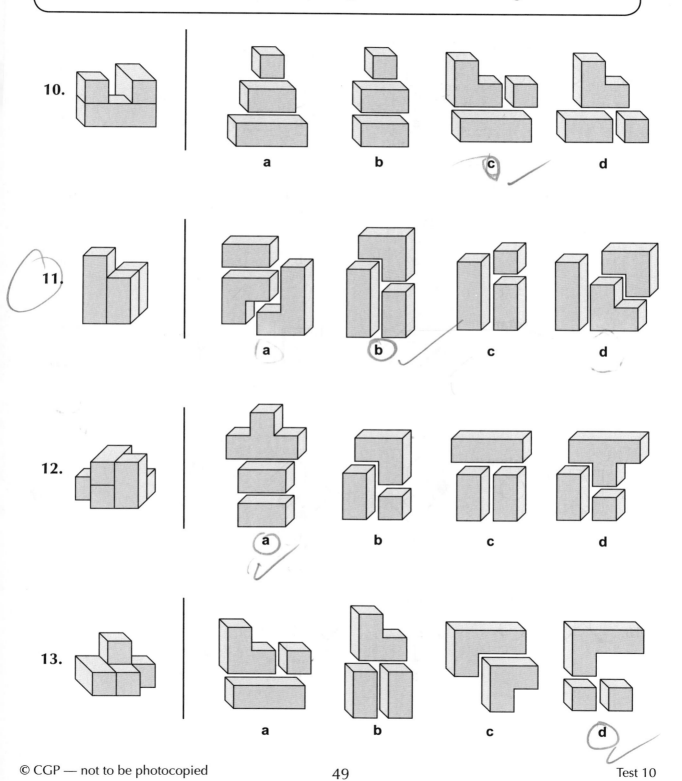

10.

a   b   c   d

11.

a   b   c   d

12.

a   b   c   d

13.

a   b   c   d

Work out which option would look like the figure on the left if it was rotated.

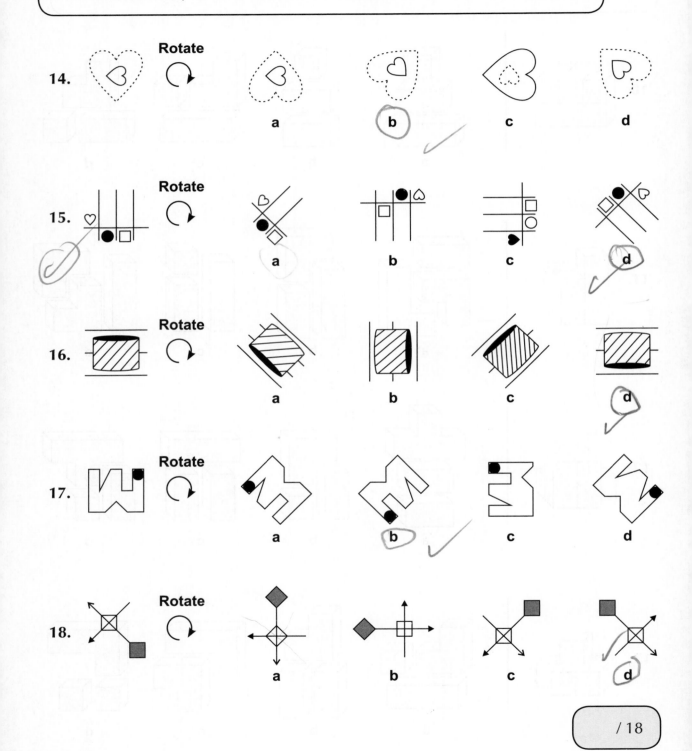

14.   Rotate   a   b   c   d

15.   Rotate   a   b   c   d

16.   Rotate   a   b   c   d

17.   Rotate   a   b   c   d

18.   Rotate   a   b   c   d

/ 18

You have **10 minutes** to do this test. Circle the letter for each correct answer.

Find the figure in each row that is most unlike the others.

1.

     a   **b**   **c**   **d**   **e**

2.

     a   **b**   **c**   **d**   **e**

3.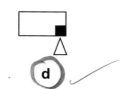

     a   **b**   **c**   **d**   **e**

4.

     a   **b**   **c**   **d**   **e**

5.

     a   **b**   **c**   **d**   **e**

© CGP — not to be photocopied

Work out which of the options best fits in place of the missing hexagon in the grid.

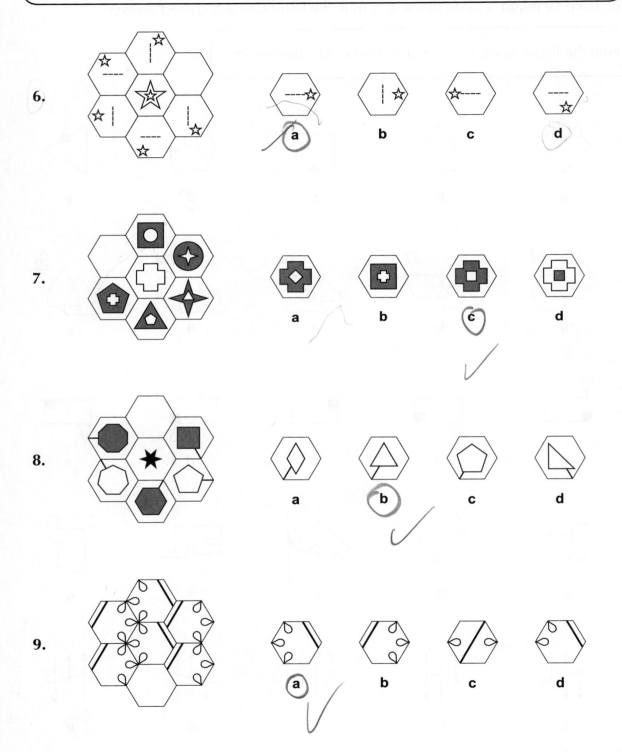

6.

a b c d

7.

a b c d

8.

a b c d

9.

a b c d

52

© CGP — not to be photocopied

Work out which 3D figure in the grey box has been rotated to make the new 3D figure.

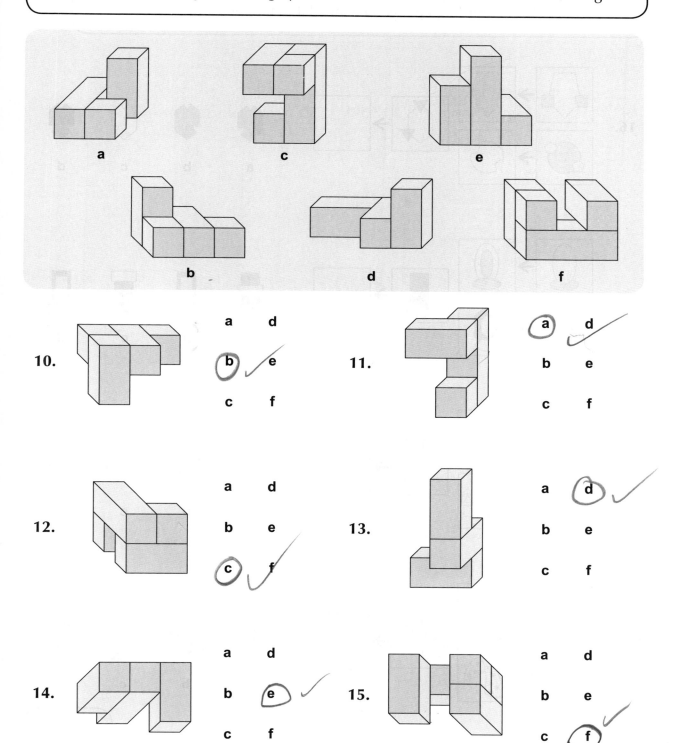

a

c

e

b

d

f

10.

a   d

b ✓   e

c   f

11.

a   d ✓

b   e

c   f

12.

a   d

b   e

c ✓   f

13.

a   d ✓

b   e

c   f

14.

a   d

b   e ✓

c   f

15.

a   d

b   e

c   f ✓

© CGP — not to be photocopied

53

Look at how the first two figures are changed, and then work out which option would look like the third figure if you changed it in the same way.

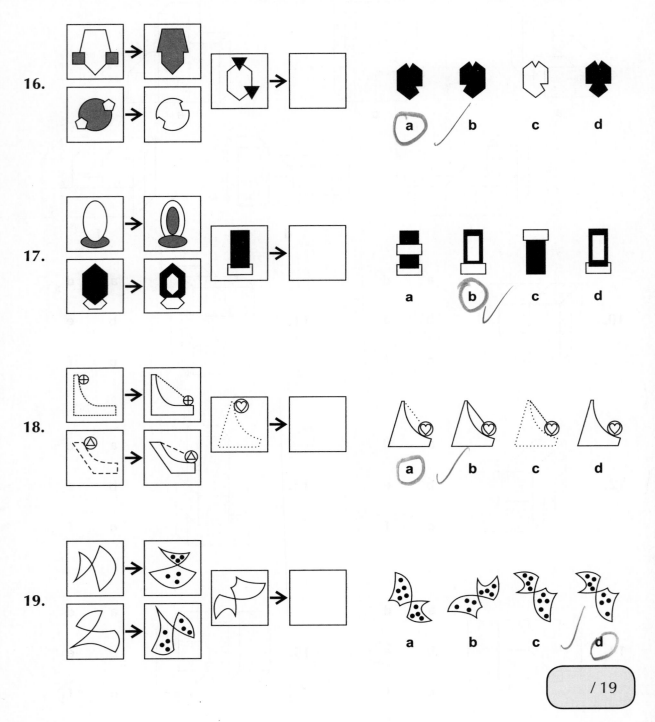

16. a

17. b ✓

18. a ✓

19. d

/ 19

54

© CGP — not to be photocopied

Test 12

You have **10 minutes** to do this test. Circle the letter for each correct answer.

Work out which option would look like the figure on the left if it was reflected over the line.

Reflect

1.

  a   b   c   d

Reflect

2.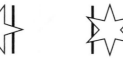

  a   b   c   d

Reflect

3.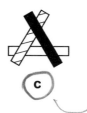

  a   b   c   d

Reflect

4.

  a   b   c   d

Reflect

5.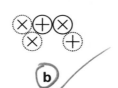

  a   b   c   d

© CGP — not to be photocopied   55

Work out which of the options best fits in place of the missing square in the grid.

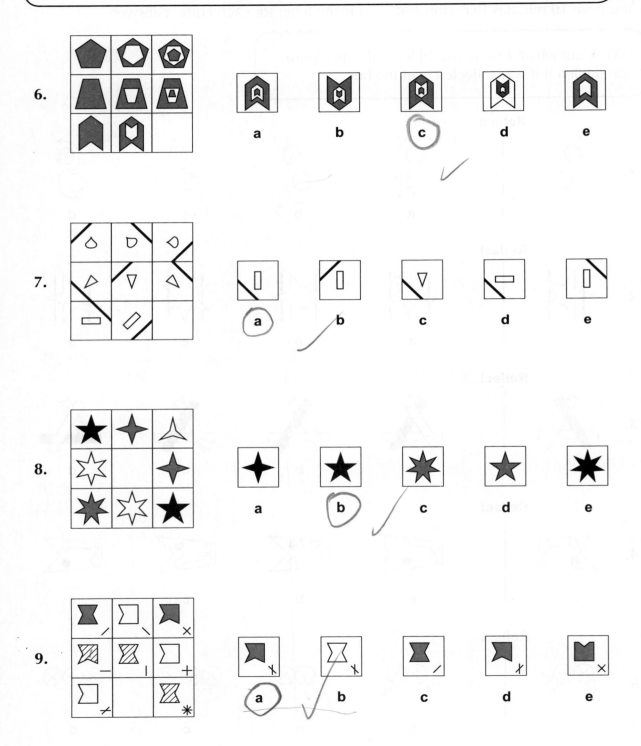

6.

7.

8.

9.

a   b   c   d   e

56

© CGP — not to be photocopied

Work out which option is most like the two figures on the left.

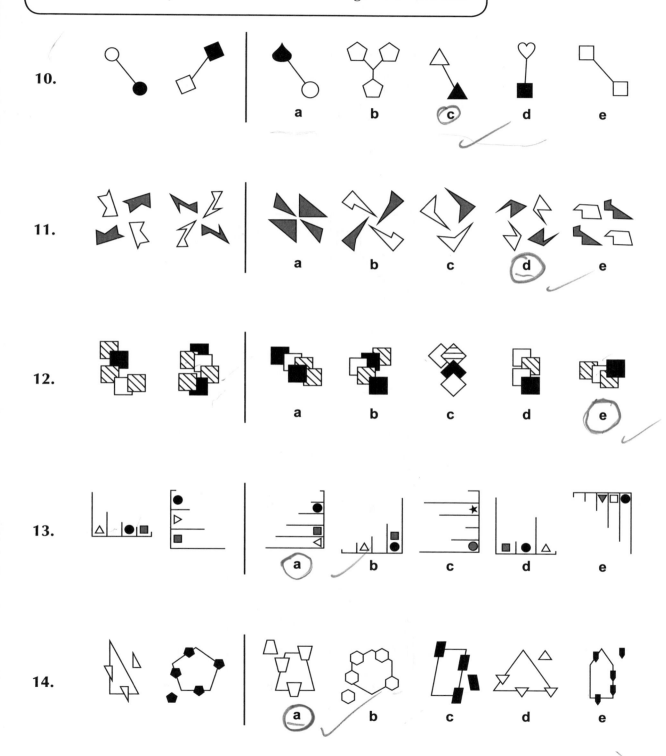

10.

    a   b   c   d   e

11.

    a   b   c   d   e

12.

    a   b   c   d   e

13.

    a   b   c   d   e

14.

    a   b   c   d   e

© CGP — not to be photocopied

Test 12

Work out which option is a top-down 2D view of the 3D figure on the left.

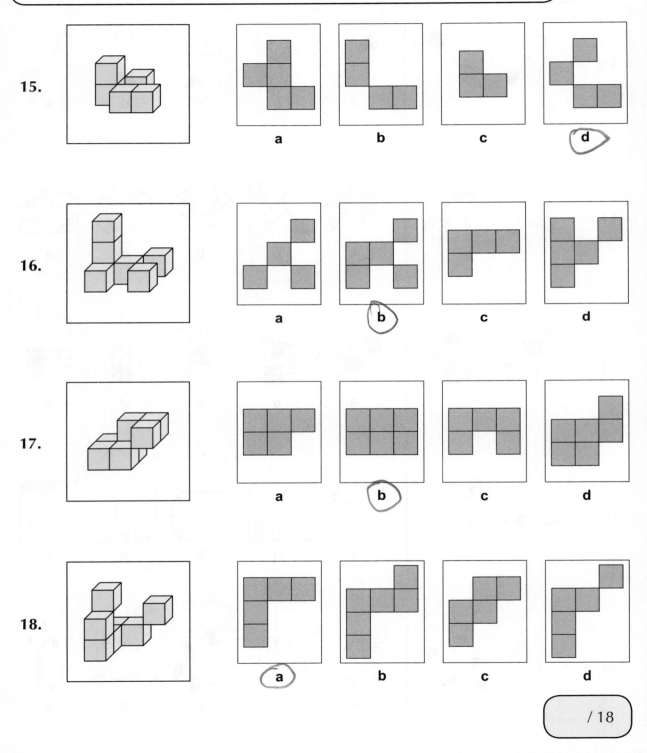

15.

a   b   c   d

16.

a   b   c   d

17.

a   b   c   d

18.

a   b   c   d

/ 18

Time for a break! These puzzles will help you spot different **shapes** and **patterns**.

Shade It!

There is a pattern hiding in this grid. To find it, shade in the squares which contain a shape with <u>any</u> of the following features:

1. Exactly 3 sides
2. A vertical line of symmetry
3. An arrow pointing up
4. Blue shading
5. The same shape twice — just rotated
6. A dashed outline

What is the pattern?

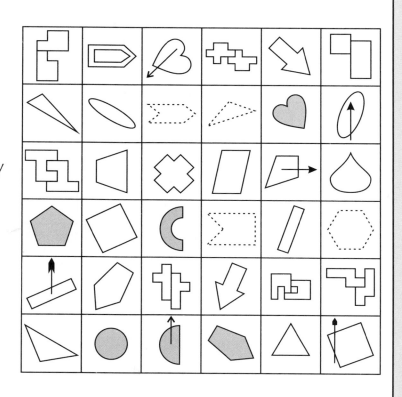

_____

Shuffled Sequences

Shown below are five sequences which have all been split up. Fill in the table to show which letter matches each number.

    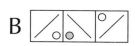  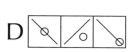 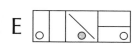

1	
2	
3	
4	
5	

© CGP — not to be photocopied

Test 13

You have **10 minutes** to do this test. Circle the letter for each correct answer.

Work out which 3D figure in the grey box has been rotated to make the new 3D figure.

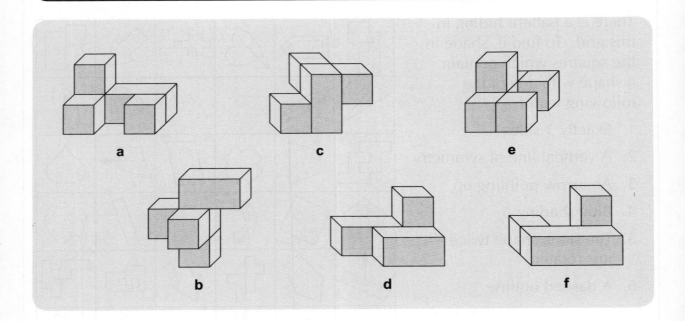

a

c

e

b

d

f

1.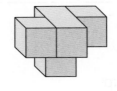

a	d
b	e
c	f

2.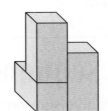

a	**d**
b	e
c	f

3.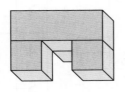

a	d
b	**e**
c	f

4.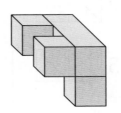

a	d
b	e
c	f

60

© CGP — not to be photocopied

Work out which of the options best fits in place of the missing square in the series.

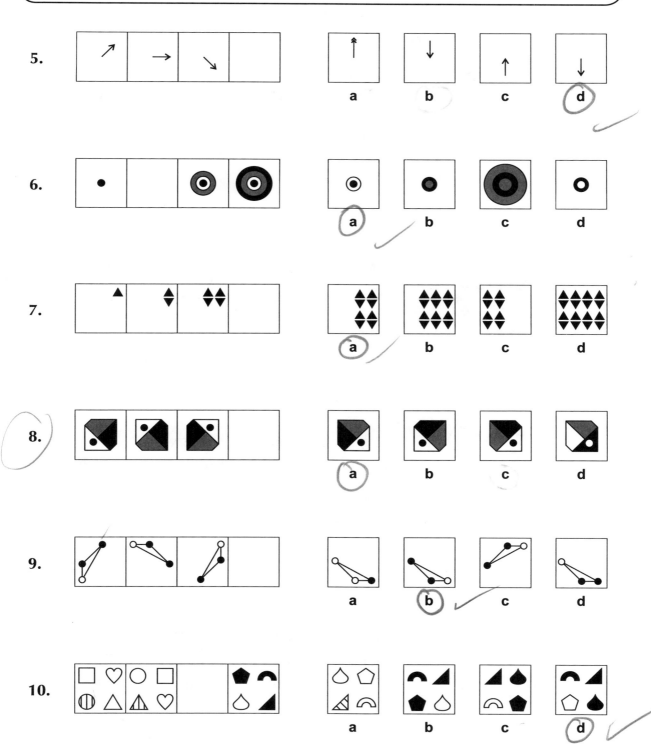

Work out which of the options best fits in place of the missing hexagon in the grid.

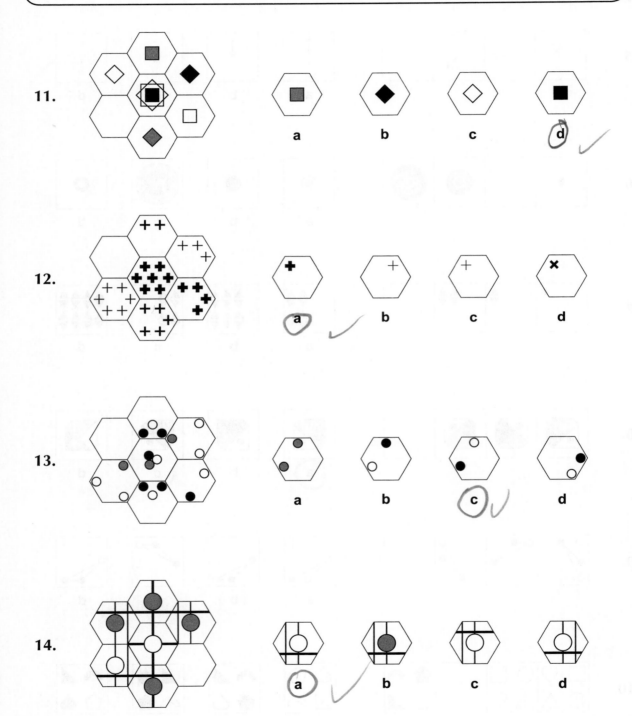

11.

a   b   c   d ✓

12.

a ✓   b   c   d

13.

a   b   c ✓   d

14.

a ✓   b   c   d

62   © CGP — not to be photocopied

Find the figure in each row that is most unlike the others.

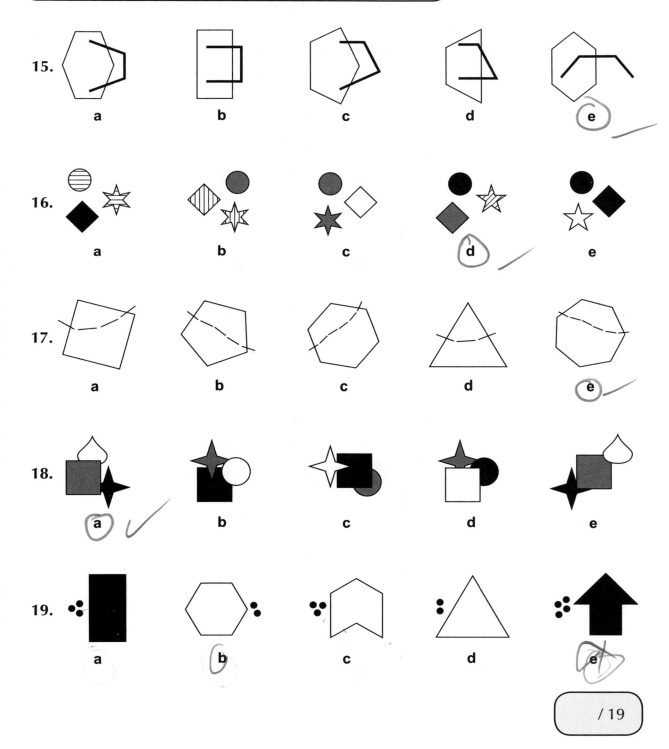

15. a   b   c   d   e

16. a   b   c   d   e

17. a   b   c   d   e

18. a   b   c   d   e

19. a   b   c   d   e

/ 19

© CGP — not to be photocopied

63

Test 14

You have **10 minutes** to do this test. Circle the letter for each correct answer.

> Work out which option is most like the three figures on the left.

1. |

  a   **b**   c   d   e

2. |

  a   **b**   c   d   e

3. 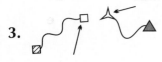 |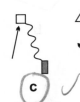

  a   b   **c**   d   e

4. 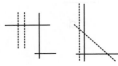 |

  a   b   **c**   d   e

5. |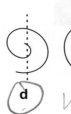

  a   b   c   **d**   e

Work out which option is a top-down 2D view of the 3D figure on the left.

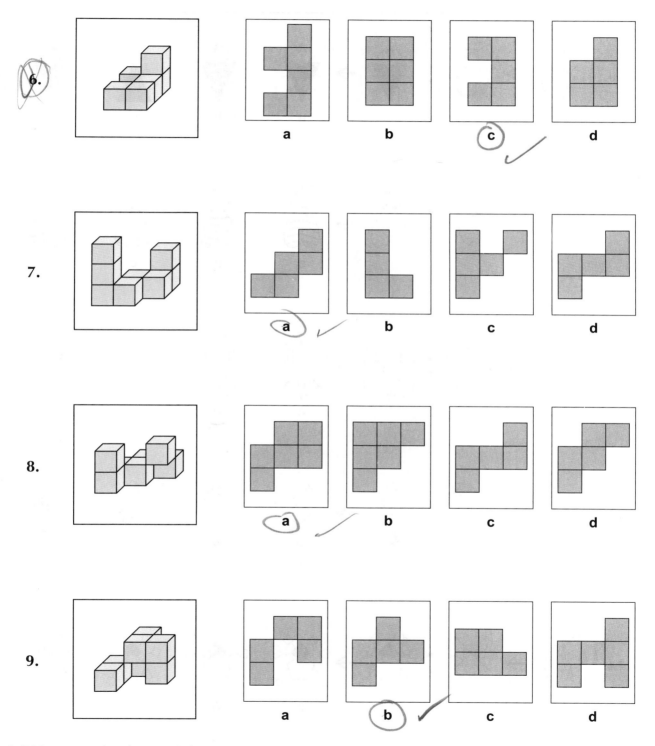

6.

a   b   c   d

7.

a   b   c   d

8.

a   b   c   d

9.

a   b   c   d

© CGP — not to be photocopied

Test 14

Look at how the first bug changes to become the second bug. Then work out which option would look like the third bug if you changed it in the same way.

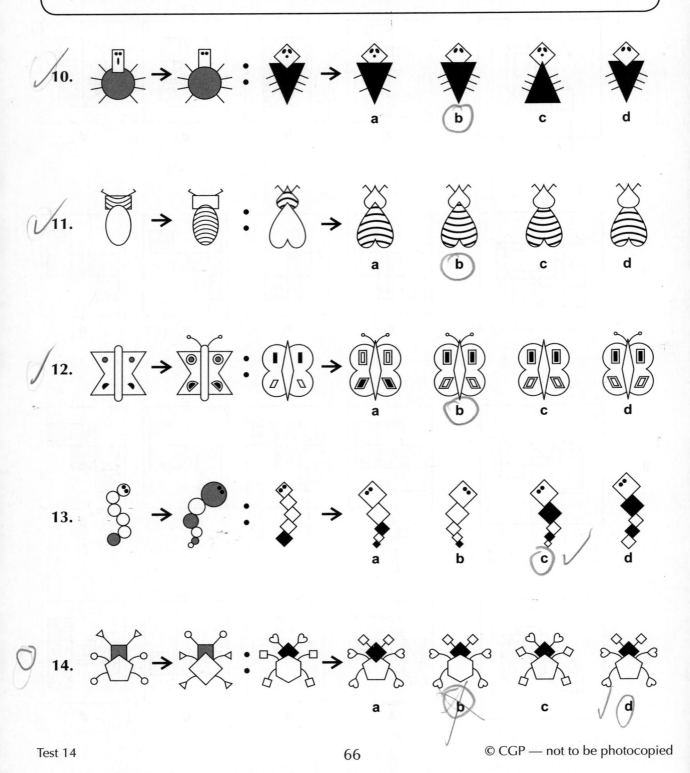

10.

     a   b   c   d

11.

     a   b   c   d

12.

     a   b   c   d

13.

     a   b   c   d

14.

     a   b   c   d

© CGP — not to be photocopied

Work out which of the options best fits in place of the missing square in the series.

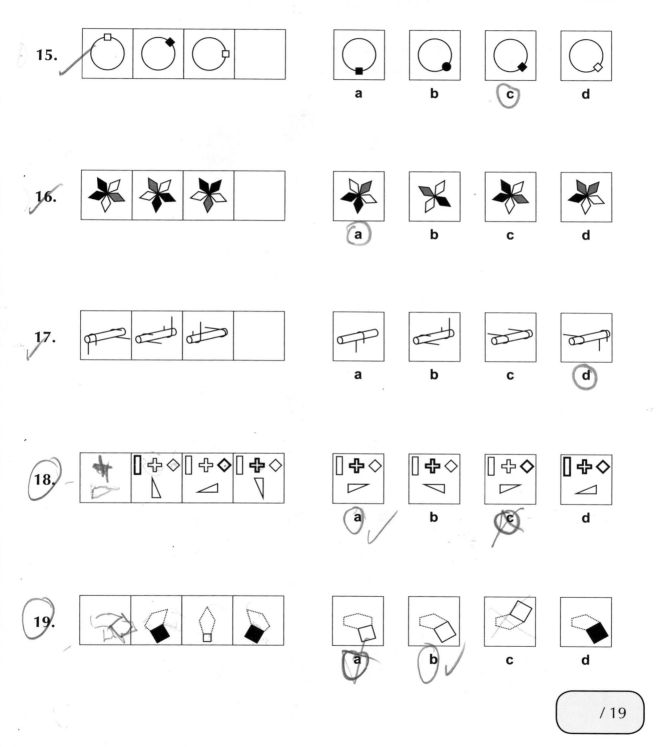

15.

    a   b   c   d

16.

    a   b   c   d

17.

    a   b   c   d

18.

    a   b   c   d

19.

    a   b   c   d

/ 19

© CGP — not to be photocopied

67

Test 14

You have **10 minutes** to do this test. Circle the letter for each correct answer.

> Work out which option is most like the two figures on the left.

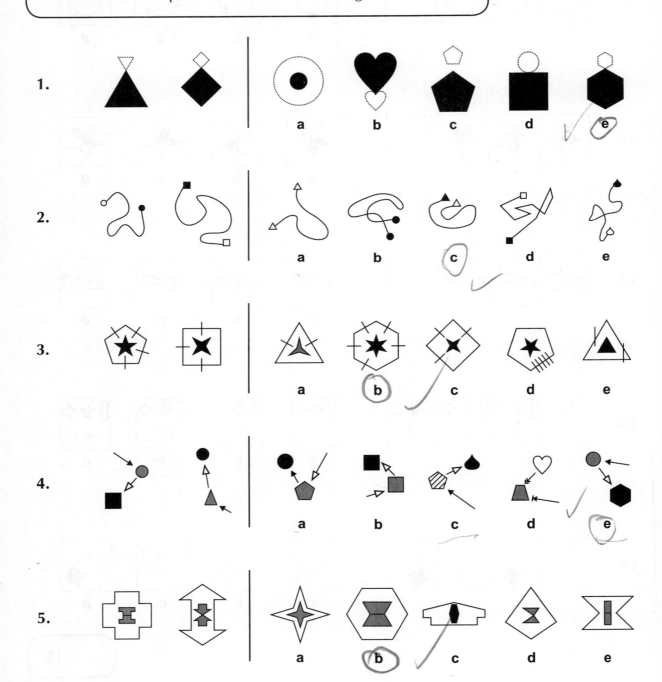

68

© CGP — not to be photocopied

Work out which of the options best fits in place of the missing square in the grid.

6. 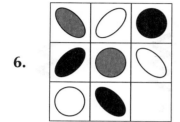   a   b   c   d   e

7. 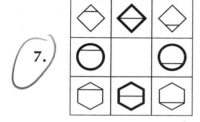   a   b   c   d e

8. 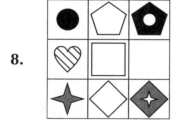   a   b  c d   e

9. 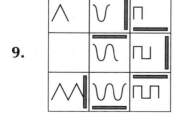   a   b   c   d   e

© CGP — not to be photocopied
Test 15

Work out which option would look like the figure on the left if it was reflected over the line.

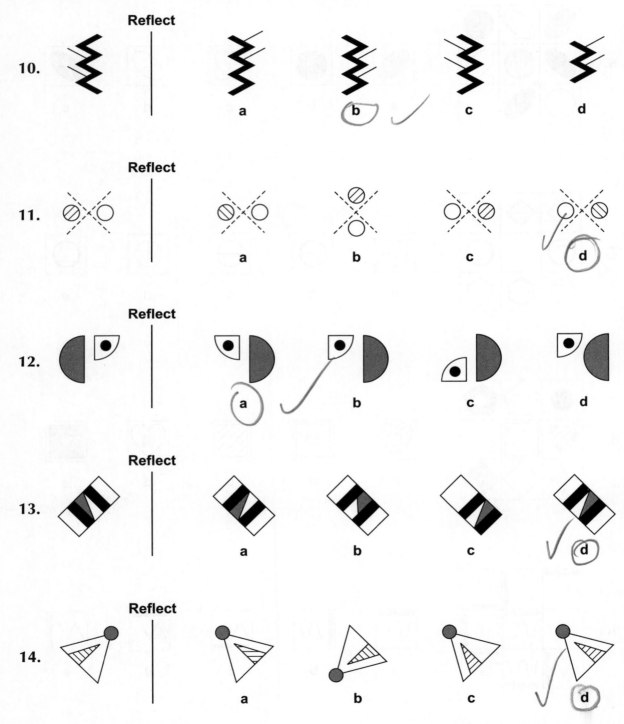

10. Reflect

a   b   c   d

11. Reflect

a   b   c   d

12. Reflect

a   b   c   d

13. Reflect

a   b   c   d

14. Reflect

a   b   c   d

Work out which set of blocks can be put together to make the 3D figure on the left.

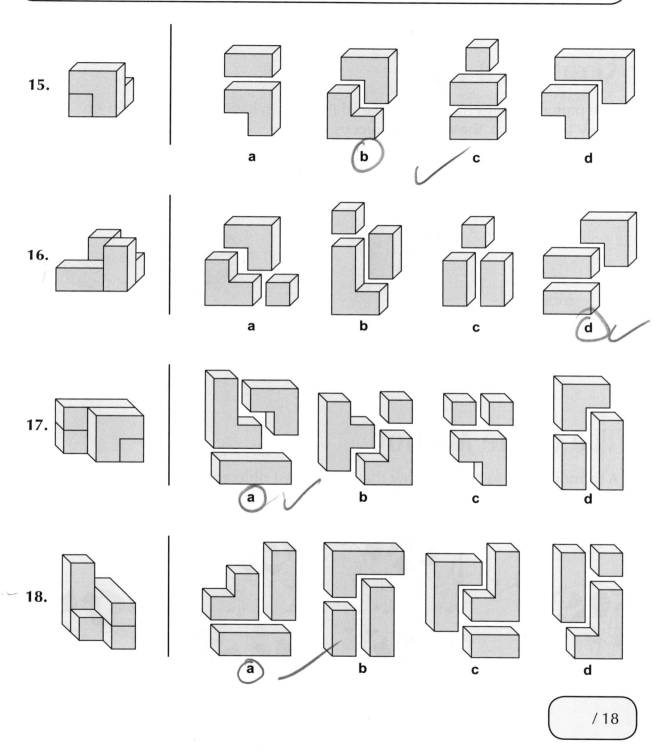

15.

a   b   c   d

16.

a   b   c   d

17.

a   b   c   d

18.

a   b   c   d

/ 18

Time for a break! These puzzles are a great way to practise **comparing** things.

Scrambled Eggs

Five patterned eggs have cracked and the pieces have become mixed up.
Draw lines to link the matching pieces together.

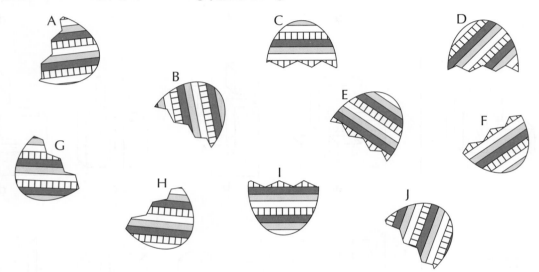

The Cattle Auction

A farmer wants to buy the cow that looks most different from all the others.
Draw a circle round the cow that she should buy.

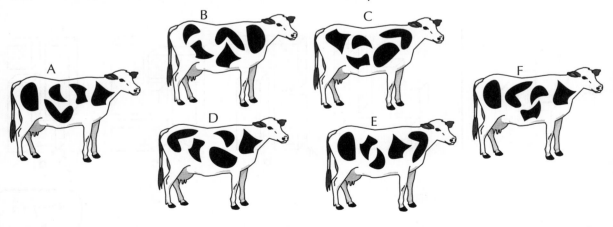

72

© CGP — not to be photocopied

Test 16

You have **10 minutes** to do this test. Circle the letter for each correct answer.

Find the figure in each row that is most unlike the others.

1.

    a   b   c   d   e

2.

    a   b   c   d   e

3.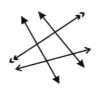

    a   b   c   d   e

4.

    a   b   c   d   e

5.

    a   b   c   d   e

Work out which of the four cubes can be made from the net.

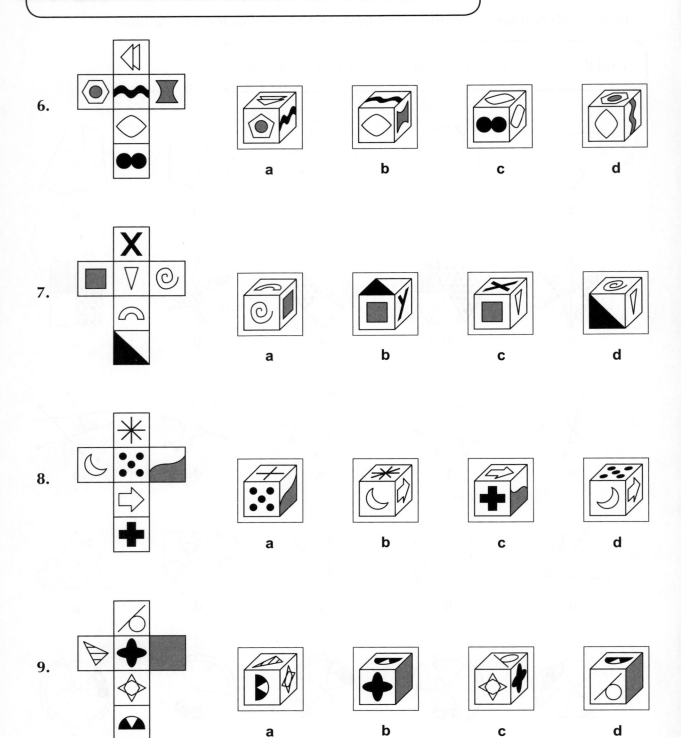

6.

    a   b   c   d

7.

    a   b   c   d

8.

    a   b   c   d

9.

    a   b   c   d

Work out which option would look like the figure on the left if it was rotated.

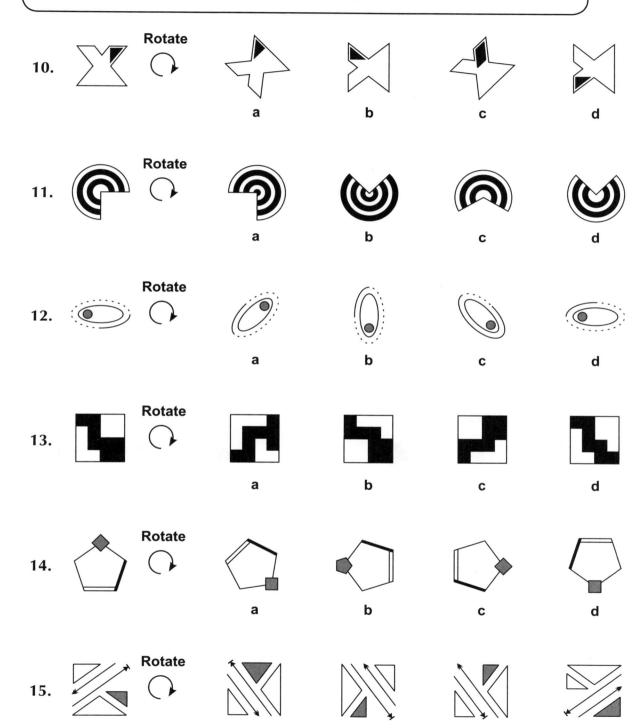

10.

Rotate

a   b   c   d

11.

Rotate

a   b   c   d

12.

Rotate

a   b   c   d

13.

Rotate

a   b   c   d

14.

Rotate

a   b   c   d

15.

Rotate

a   b   c   d

© CGP — not to be photocopied   75   Test 16

Work out which of the options best fits in place of the missing square in the grid.

16.

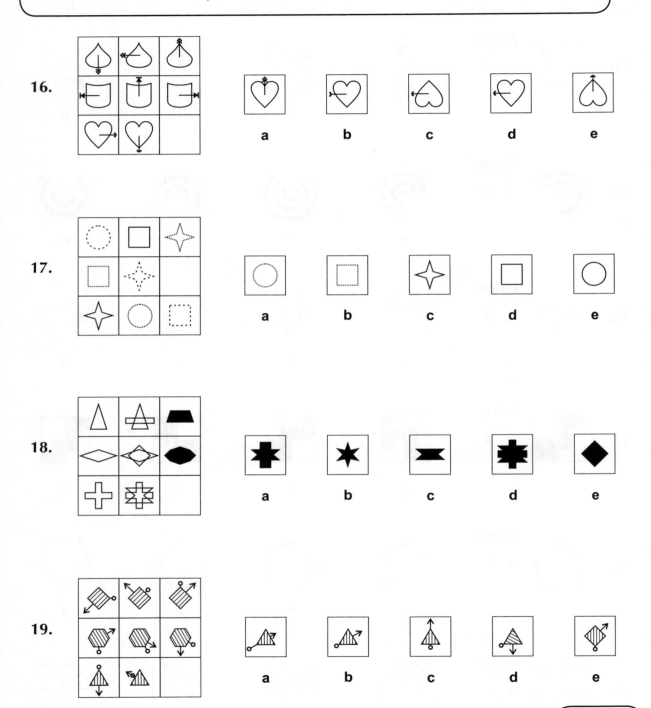

a   b   c   d   e

17.

a   b   c   d   e

18.

a   b   c   d   e

19.

a   b   c   d   e

/ 19

© CGP — not to be photocopied

Test 17

You have **10 minutes** to do this test. Circle the letter for each correct answer.

Look at how the first two figures are changed, and then work out which option would look like the third figure if you changed it in the same way.

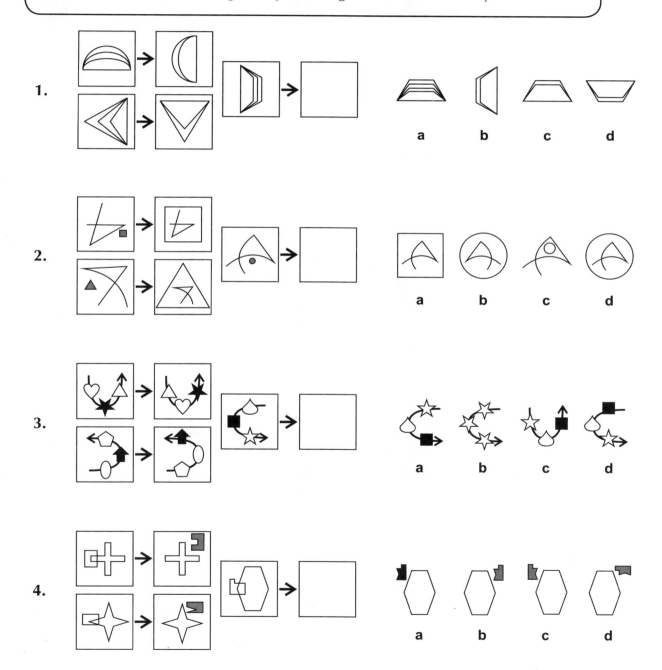

1.   a   b   c   d

2.   a   b   c   d

3.   a   b   c   d

4.   a   b   c   d

© CGP — not to be photocopied   77

Work out which option would look like the figure on the left if it was reflected over the line.

Reflect

5.

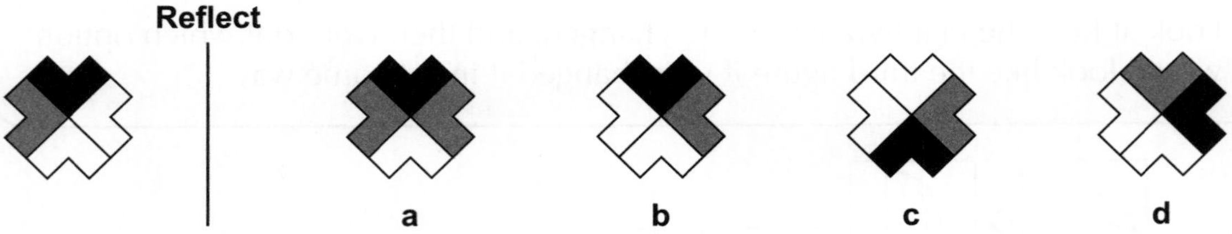

a   b   c   d

Reflect

6.

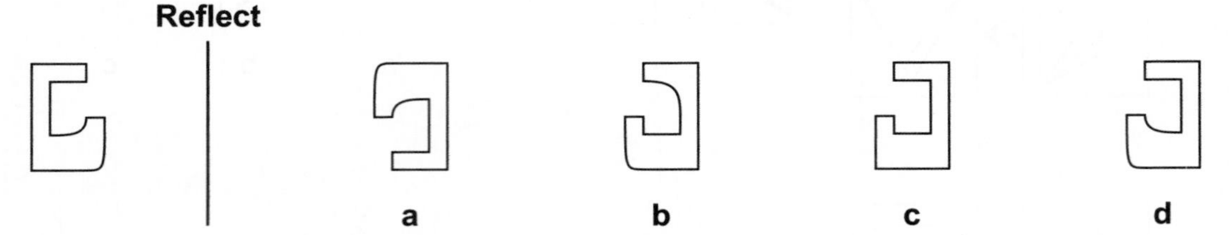

a   b   c   d

Reflect

7.

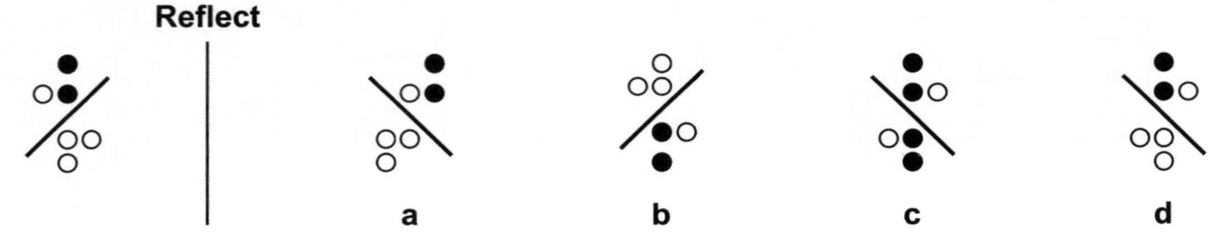

a   b   c   d

Reflect

8.

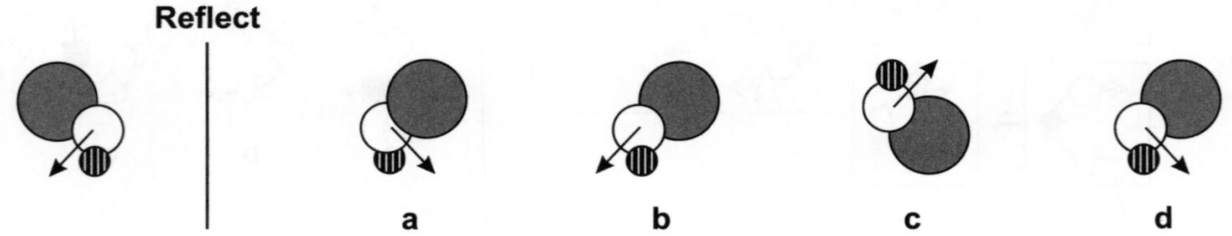

a   b   c   d

Reflect

9.

a   b   c   d

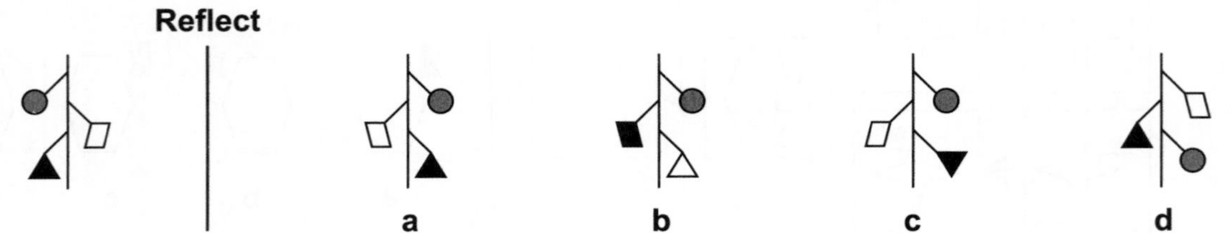

© CGP — not to be photocopied

Work out which of the four cubes can be made from the net.

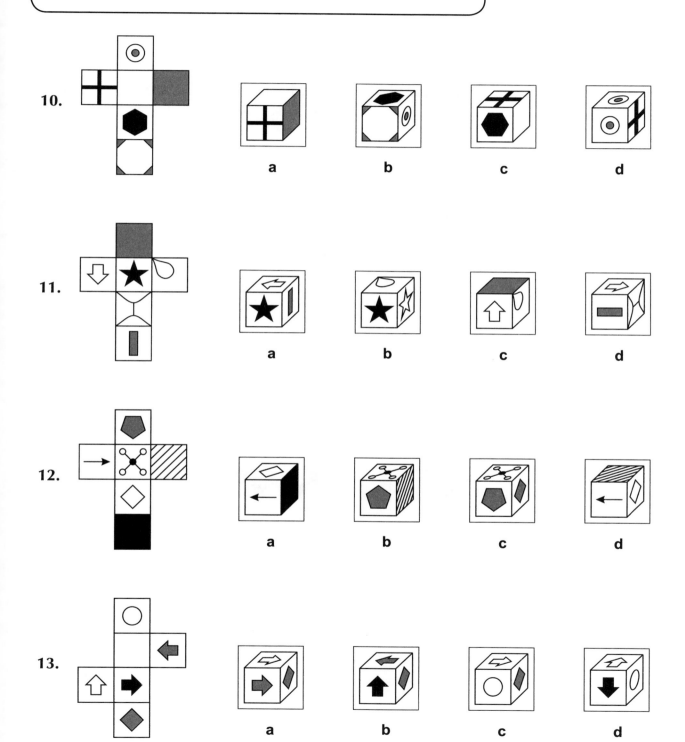

10.

a   b   c   d

11.

a   b   c   d

12.

a   b   c   d

13.

a   b   c   d

© CGP — not to be photocopied

Test 17

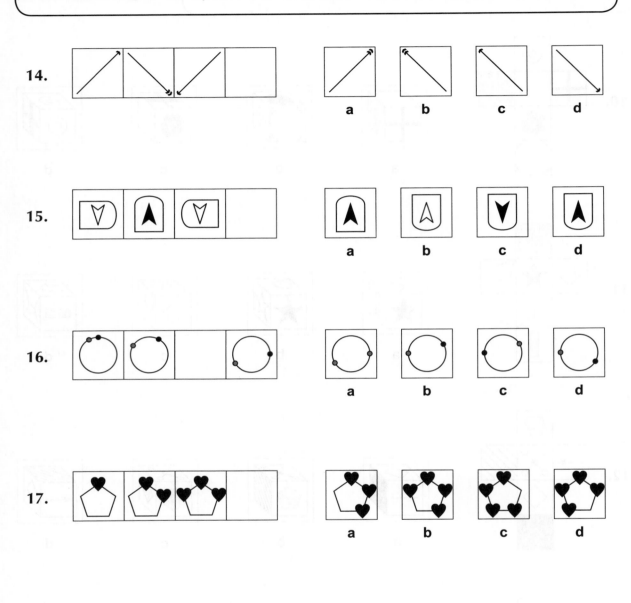

14.   a   b   c   d

15.   a   b   c   d

16.   a   b   c   d

17.   a   b   c   d

18.   a   b   c   d

/ 18

© CGP — not to be photocopied

You have **10 minutes** to do this test. Circle the letter for each correct answer.

> Work out which option would look like the figure
> on the left if it was reflected over the line.

Reflect

1.

                    a   **b**   **c**   **d**

Reflect

2.

                    a   **b**   **c**   **d**

Reflect

3.

                    a   **b**   **c**   **d**

Reflect

4.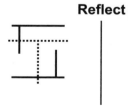

                    a   **b**   **c**   **d**

Reflect

5.

                    a   **b**   **c**   **d**

© CGP — not to be photocopied   81   Test 18

Find the figure in each row that is most unlike the others.

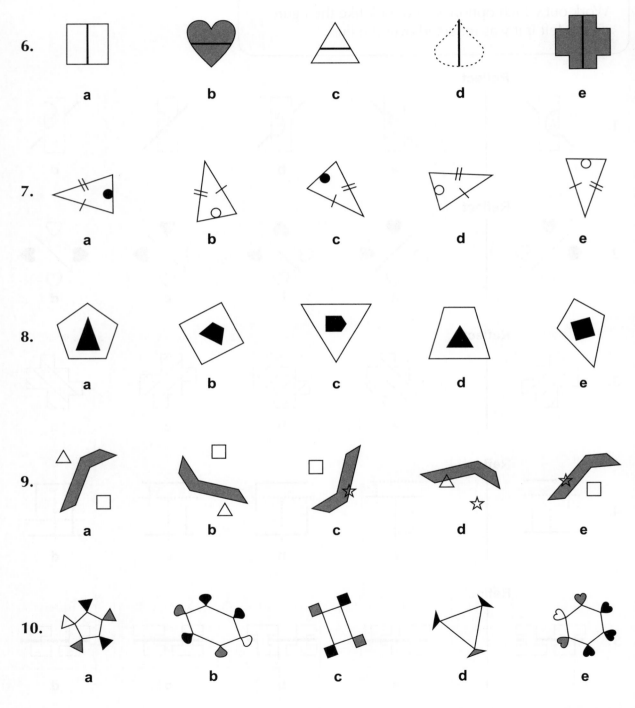

82

© CGP — not to be photocopied

Work out which option is a top-down 2D view of the 3D figure on the left.

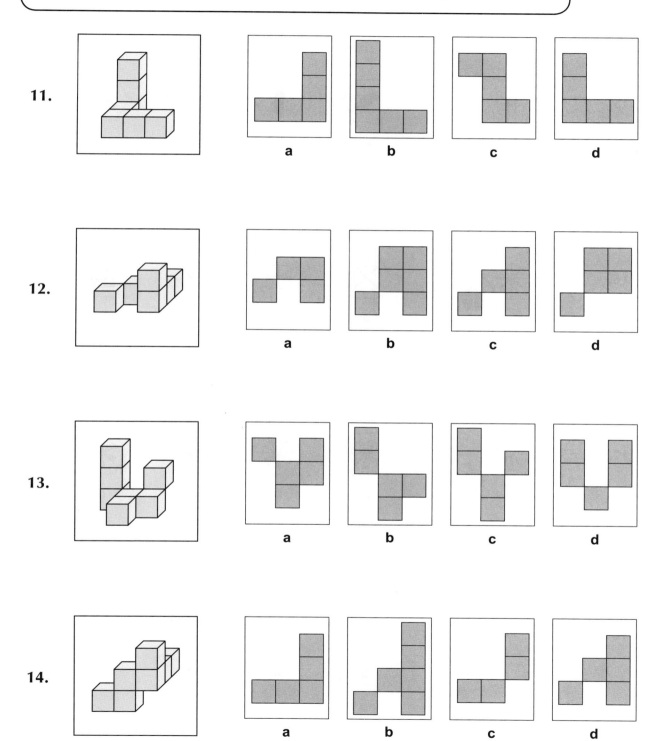

11.

a   b   c   d

12.

a   b   c   d

13.

a   b   c   d

14.

a   b   c   d

© CGP — not to be photocopied

Test 18

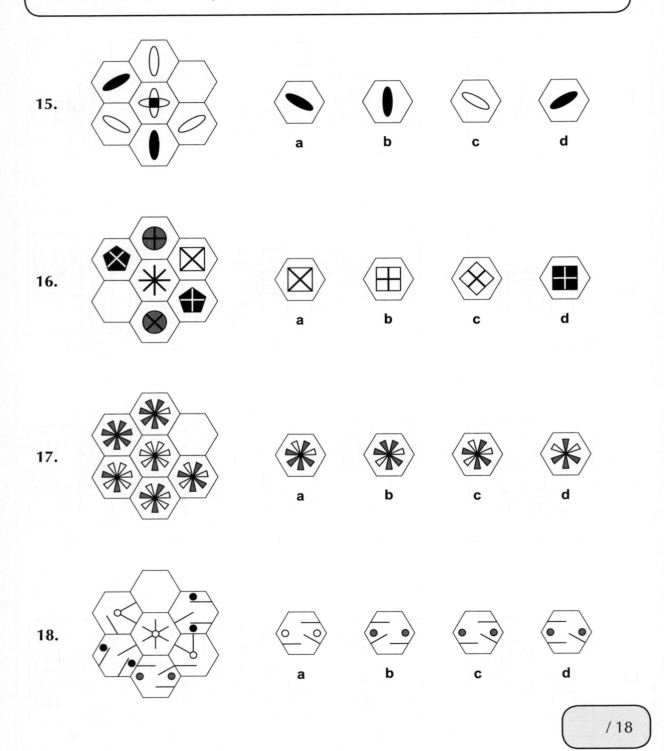

15.

a   b   c   d

16.

a   b   c   d

17.

a   b   c   d

18.

a   b   c   d

/ 18

84

© CGP — not to be photocopied

Puzzles 6

Have a go at these puzzles — they're a great way to practise **spotting patterns**.

Sailing the Seas

Sailor Sue wants to visit five different islands. She wants the flags of the islands she visits to follow a sequence. On the map below, draw out Sailor Sue's route — her boat is next to the first island she visits.

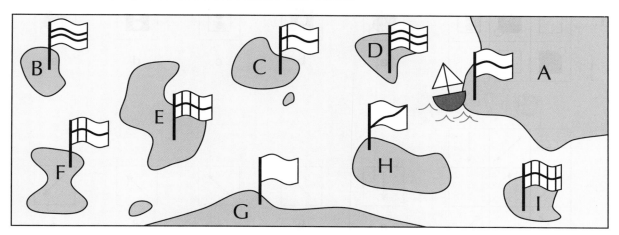

Train Track Troubles

The grid below contains train tracks, but some of the squares are missing.
The five empty spaces are marked with a letter.
Write the letter of the space where each square should go.

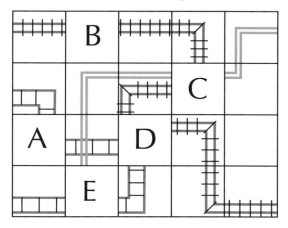

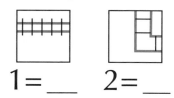

1 = ___   2 = ___

3 = ___   4 = ___   5 = ___

© CGP — not to be photocopied

Puzzles 6

🕙 10

You have **10 minutes** to do this test. Circle the letter for each correct answer.

Work out which of the options best fits in place of the missing square in the grid.

1.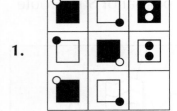

   a   b   c   d   e

2.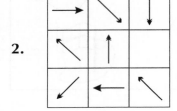

   a   b   c   d   e

3.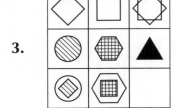

   a   b   c   d   e

4.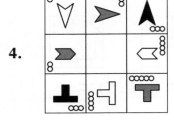

   a   b   c   d   e

© CGP — not to be photocopied

Look at how the first two figures are changed, and then work out which option would look like the third figure if you changed it in the same way.

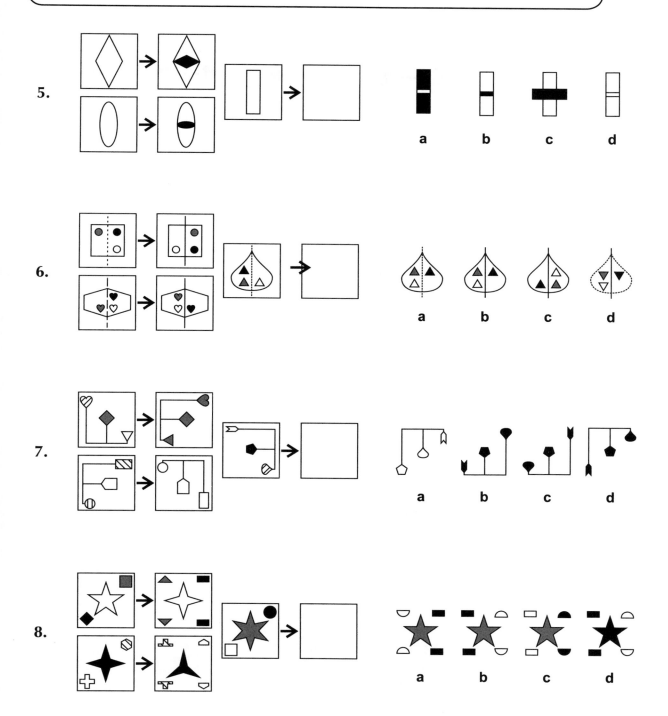

5.

a   b   c   d

6.

a   b   c   d

7.

a   b   c   d

8.

a   b   c   d

© CGP — not to be photocopied

Test 19

Work out which option would look like the figure on the left if it was reflected over the line.

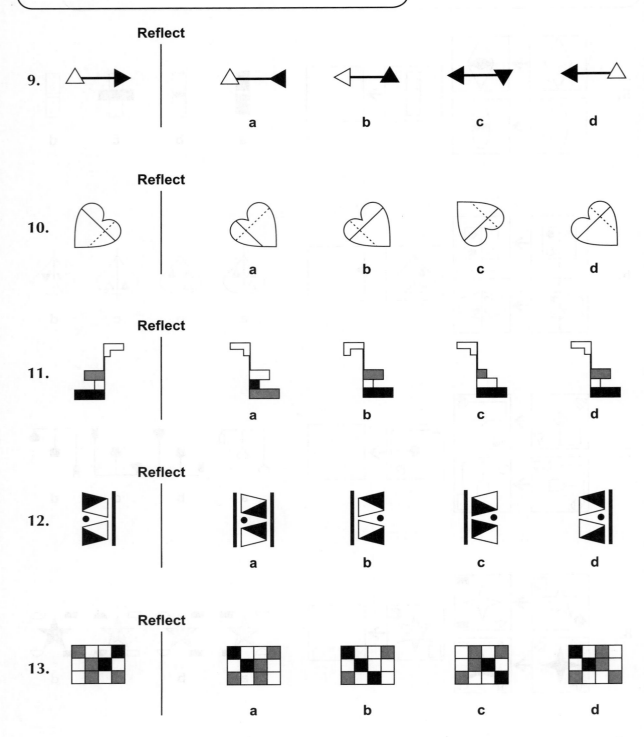

9.

Reflect

a   b   c   d

10.

Reflect

a   b   c   d

11.

Reflect

a   b   c   d

12.

Reflect

a   b   c   d

13.

Reflect

a   b   c   d

Test 19   88   © CGP — not to be photocopied

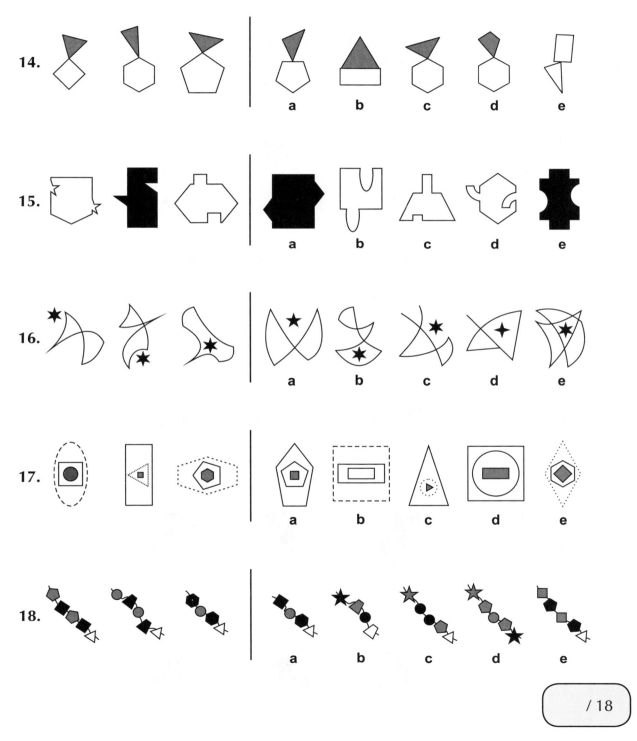

14.

a   b   c   d   e

15.

a   b   c   d   e

16.

a   b   c   d   e

17.

a   b   c   d   e

18.

a   b   c   d   e

/ 18

© CGP — not to be photocopied

Test 20

You have **10 minutes** to do this test. Circle the letter for each correct answer.

Work out which option would look like the figure on the left if it was reflected over the line.

Reflect

1.

                                             a   b   c   d

Reflect

2.

                                             a   b   c   d

Reflect

3.

                                             a   b   c   d

Reflect

4.

                                             a   b   c   d

Reflect

5.

                                             a   b   c   d

 © CGP — not to be photocopied

Work out which of the options best fits in place of the missing hexagon in the grid.

6.

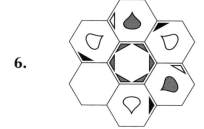

a

b

c

d

7.

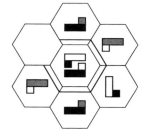

a

b

c

d

8.

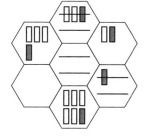

a

b

c

d

9.

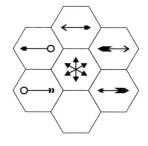

a

b

c

d

Work out which option is most like the two figures on the left.

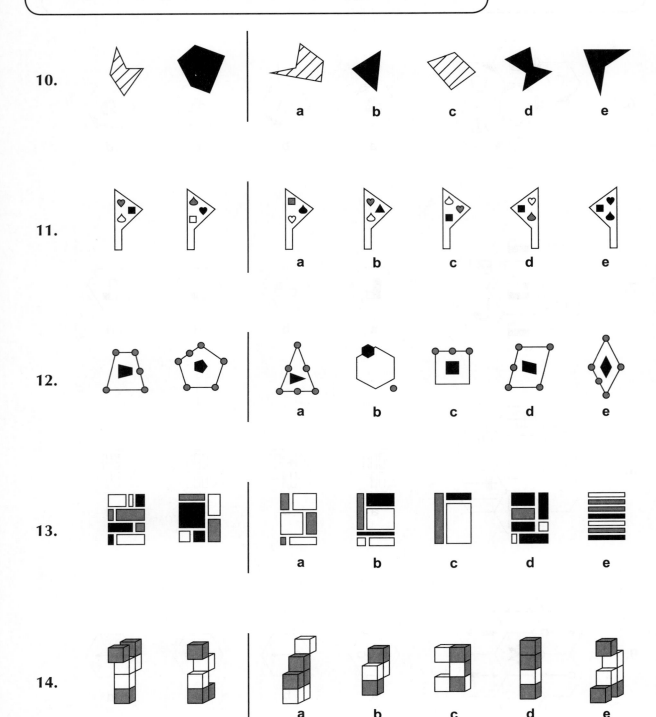

10.

    a   b   c   d   e

11.

12.

13.

14.

92

© CGP — not to be photocopied

Work out which 3D figure in the grey box has been rotated to make the new 3D figure.

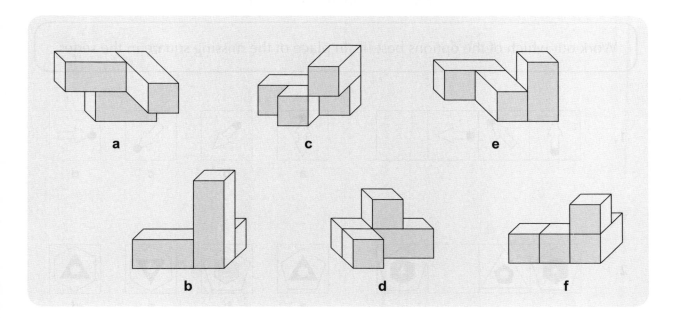

a

c

e

b

d

f

15.
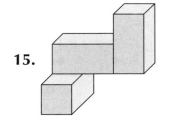

a   d

b   e

c   f

16.

a   d

b   e

c   f

17.
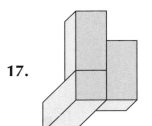

a   d

b   e

c   f

18.
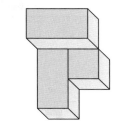

a   d

b   e

c   f

/ 18

© CGP — not to be photocopied

93

You have **10 minutes** to do this test. Circle the letter for each correct answer.

> Work out which of the options best fits in place of the missing square in the series.

1.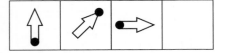
   a   b   c   d

2.
   a   b   c   d

3.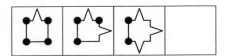
   a   b   c   d

4.
   a   b   c   d

5.
   a   b   c   d

94   © CGP — not to be photocopied

Work out which of the options best fits in place of the missing square in the grid.

6.

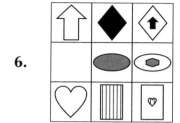

                                a   **b**   **c**   **d**   **e**

7.

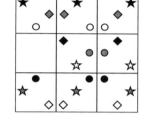

                                a   **b**   **c**   **d**   **e**

8.

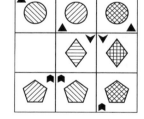

                                a   **b**   **c**   **d**   **e**

9.

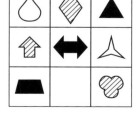

                                a   **b**   **c**   **d**   **e**

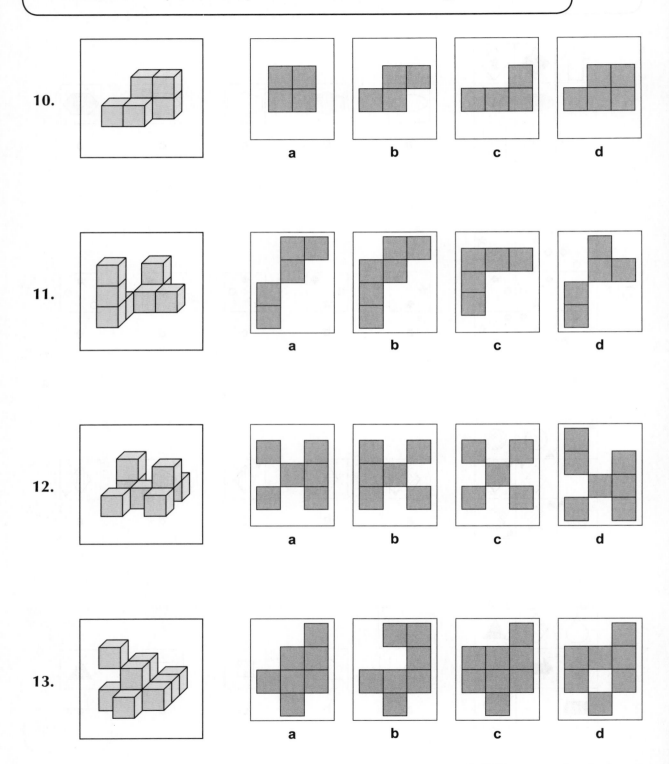

10.

a   b   c   d

11.

a   b   c   d

12.

a   b   c   d

13.

a   b   c   d

© CGP — not to be photocopied

Work out which option would look like the figure on the left if it was rotated.

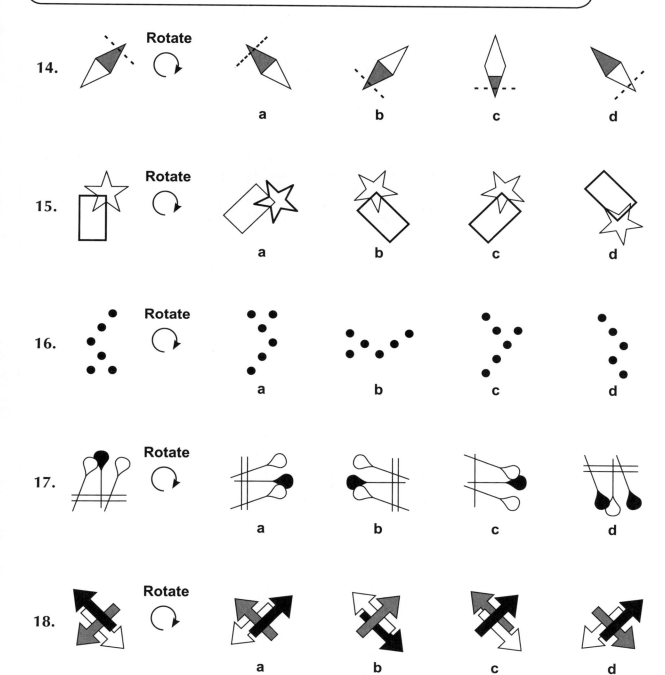

14. Rotate

a   b   c   d

15. Rotate

a   b   c   d

16. Rotate

a   b   c   d

17. Rotate

a   b   c   d

18. Rotate

a   b   c   d

/ 18

© CGP — not to be photocopied

Test 21

These puzzles are brilliant for practising all the skills you'll need — get stuck in.

Mirror, Mirror on the Wall...

Cyril looks in the mirror before going out. Circle the reflection he sees.

A   B   C   D   E

Castle Capers

A child has made a castle from blocks. Here are two views of that castle:

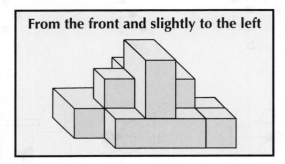

From the front and slightly to the left

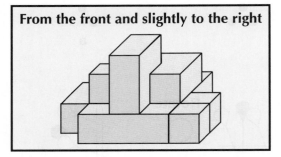

From the front and slightly to the right

Circle the correct view of the castle directly from the left-hand side...

A   B   C   D

... and directly from the right-hand side.

E   F   G   H

98

© CGP — not to be photocopied

⏱ 10

You have **10 minutes** to do this test. Circle the letter for each correct answer.

> Work out which set of blocks can be put together to make the 3D figure on the left.

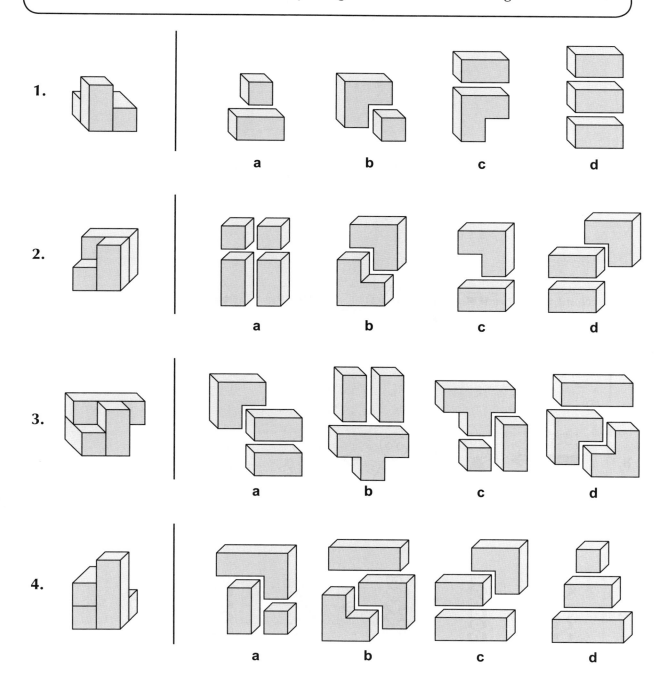

1.

a   b   c   d

2.

a   b   c   d

3.

a   b   c   d

4.

a   b   c   d

© CGP — not to be photocopied   99

Look at how the first bug changes to become the second bug. Then work out which option would look like the third bug if you changed it in the same way.

5.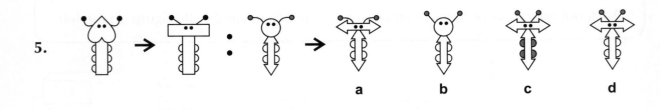

   a b c d

6.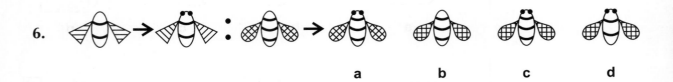

   a b c d

7.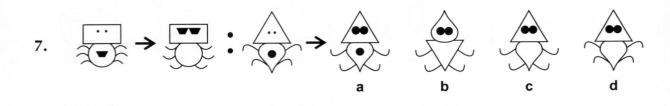

   a b c d

8.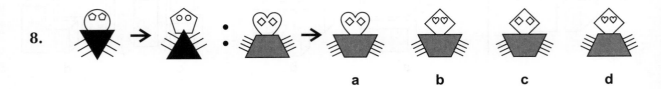

   a b c d

9.

   a b c d

Work out which of the options best fits in place of the missing square in the grid.

10. 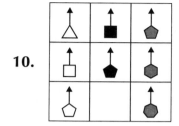

                                             a   **b**   **c**   **d**   **e**

11.

                                             a   **b**   **c**   **d**   **e**

12.

                                             a   **b**   **c**   **d**   **e**

13. 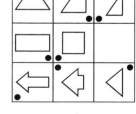

                                             a   **b**   **c**   **d**   **e**

Work out which option is most like the three figures on the left.

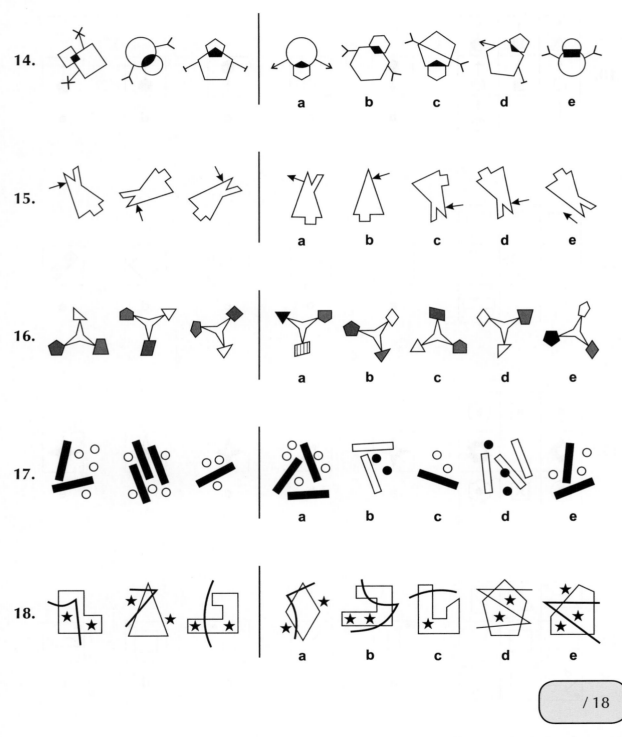

14.

a   b   c   d   e

15.

a   b   c   d   e

16.

a   b   c   d   e

17.

a   b   c   d   e

18.

a   b   c   d   e

/ 18

Test 23

You have **10 minutes** to do this test. Circle the letter for each correct answer.

Work out which of the options best fits in place of the missing hexagon in the grid.

1.

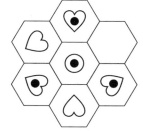

a   b   c   d

2.

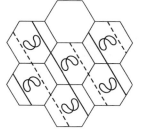

a   b   c   d

3.

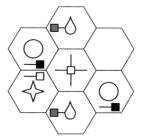

a   b   c   d

4.

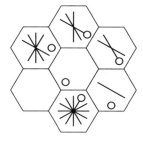

a   b   c   d

© CGP — not to be photocopied

Work out which option would look like the figure on the left if it was rotated.

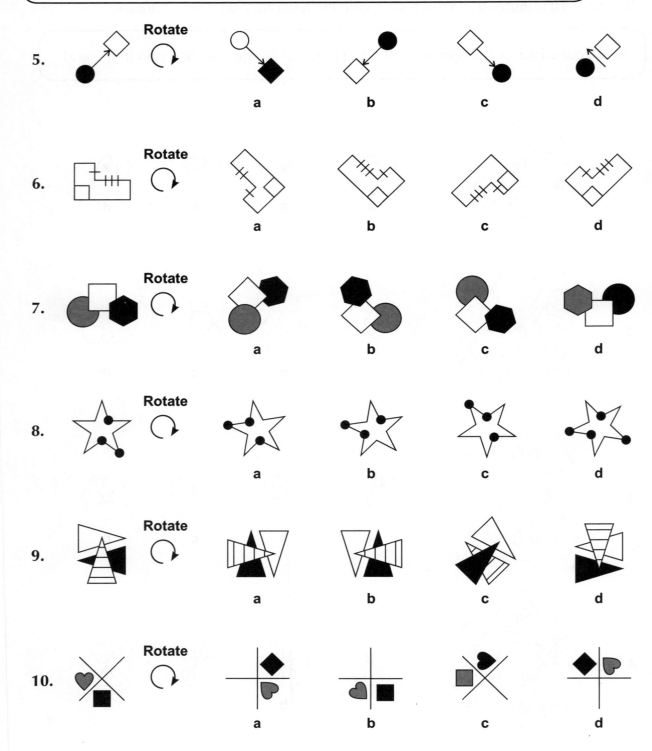

104

© CGP — not to be photocopied

Work out which of the four cubes can be made from the net.

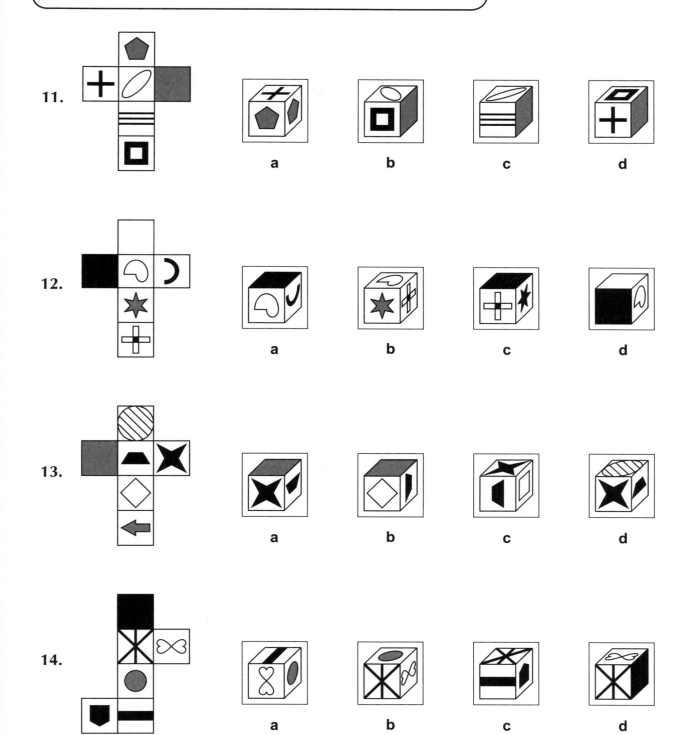

11.   **a**   **b**   **c**   **d**

12.   **a**   **b**   **c**   **d**

13.   **a**   **b**   **c**   **d**

14.   **a**   **b**   **c**   **d**

© CGP — not to be photocopied   105

Find the figure in each row that is most unlike the others.

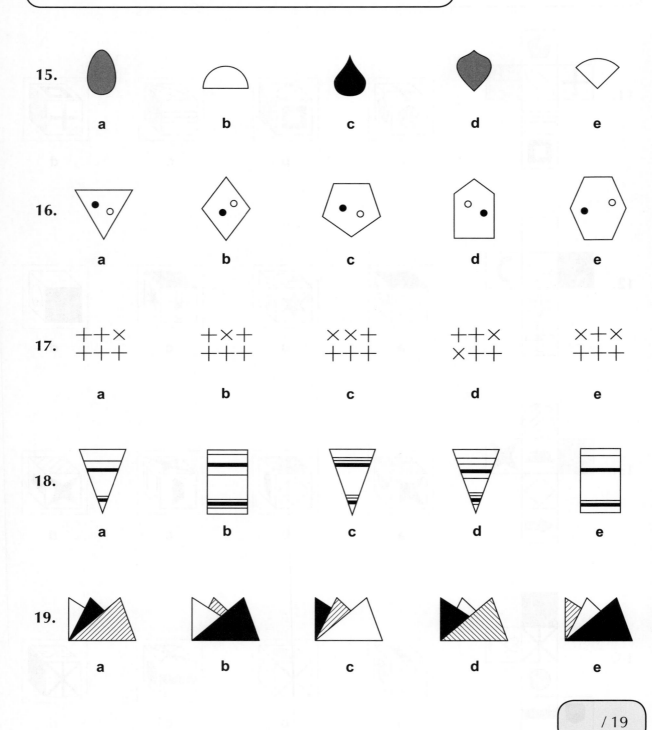

15.
a   b   c   d   e

16.
a   b   c   d   e

17.
a   b   c   d   e

18.
a   b   c   d   e

19.
a   b   c   d   e

/ 19

© CGP — not to be photocopied

Test 24

You have **10 minutes** to do this test. Circle the letter for each correct answer.

Work out which of the options best fits in place of the missing square in the series.

1.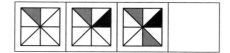

                                                    a   **b**   **c**   **d**

2.

                                                    a   **b**   **c**   **d**

3.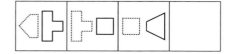

                                                    a   **b**   **c**   **d**

4.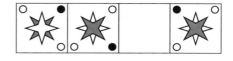

                                                    a   **b**   **c**   **d**

5.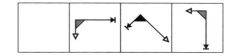

                                                    a   **b**   **c**   **d**

Work out which set of blocks can be put together to make the 3D figure on the left.

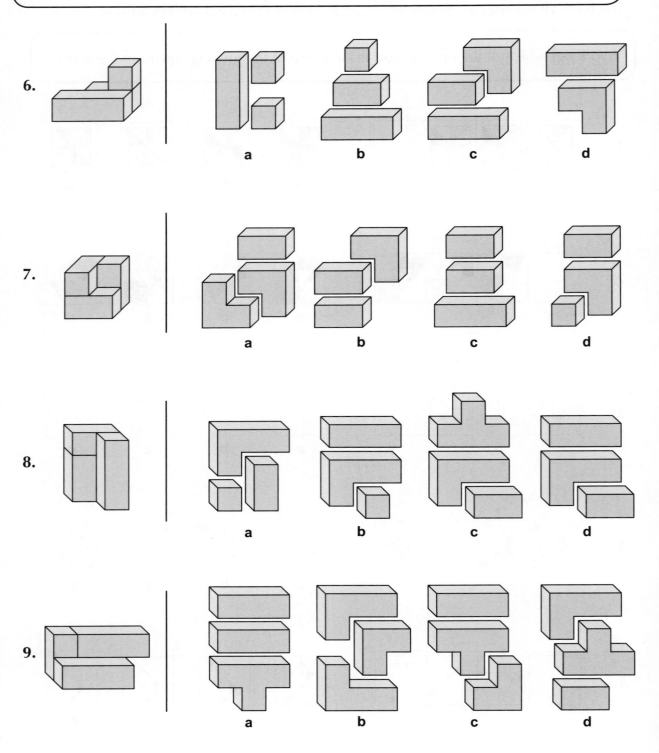

6.

a   b   c   d

7.

a   b   c   d

8.

a   b   c   d

9.

a   b   c   d

108

© CGP — not to be photocopied

Look at how the first two figures are changed, and then work out which option would look like the third figure if you changed it in the same way.

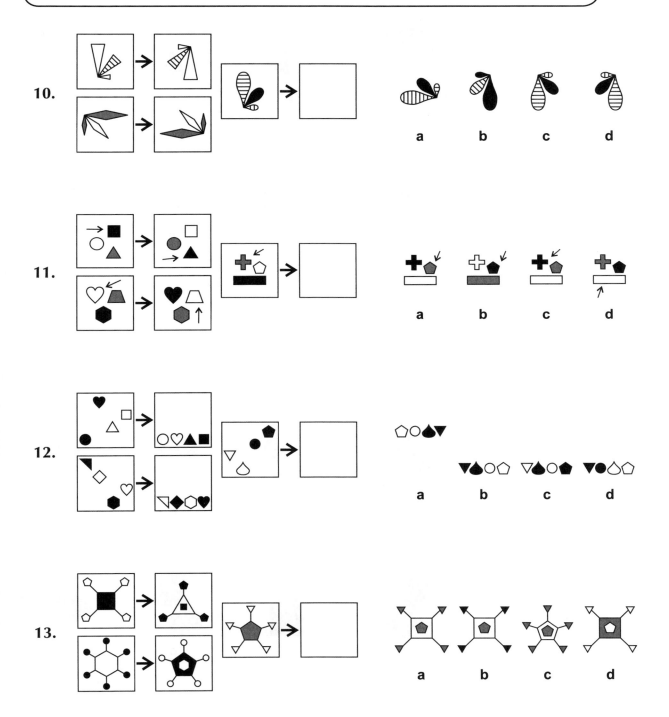

10.

a   b   c   d

11.

a   b   c   d

12.

a   b   c   d

13.

a   b   c   d

© CGP — not to be photocopied
109

Work out which option would look like the figure on the left if it was rotated.

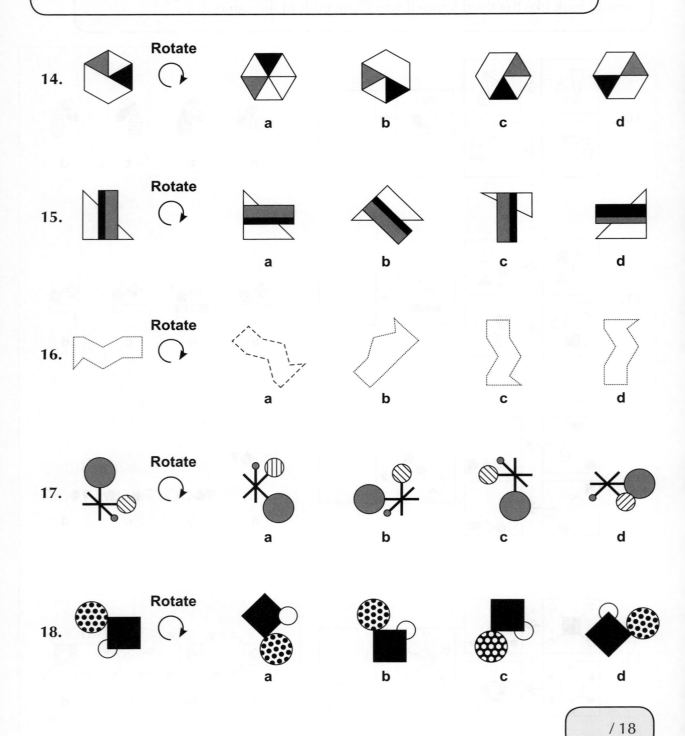

14. Rotate

a   b   c   d

15. Rotate

a   b   c   d

16. Rotate

a   b   c   d

17. Rotate

a   b   c   d

18. Rotate

a   b   c   d

/ 18

110

© CGP — not to be photocopied

Puzzles 8

It's puzzle time! This page will help you with **spotting connections** between figures.

Car Conundrum

Conor wants to buy a new car. All cars have identical wheels, but Conor wants everything else about his car to be unique. Circle the car that he should choose.

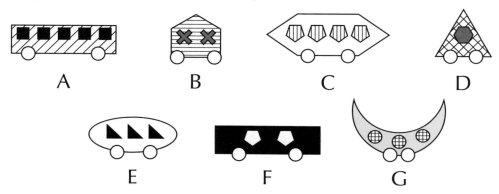

Odd Addresses

In Shapetown, addresses are related to the appearance of the houses. Match each address to its house. Then draw the address of the final house.

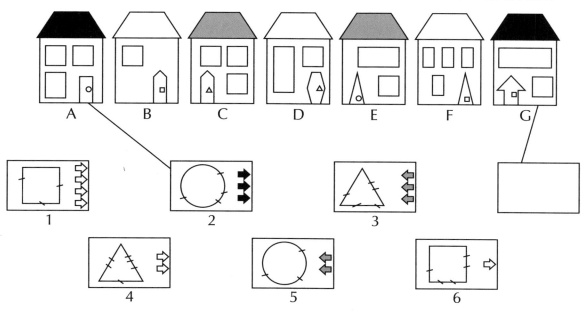

You have **10 minutes** to do this test. Circle the letter for each correct answer.

> Work out which of the options best fits in place of the missing square in the grid.

1.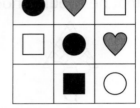

a ⬤ b ♥ c ♥ d ◼ e ♡

2.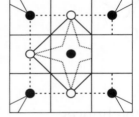

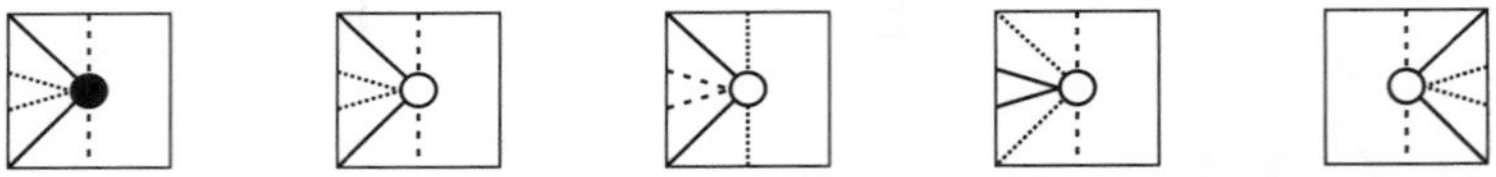

a b c d e

3.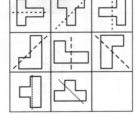

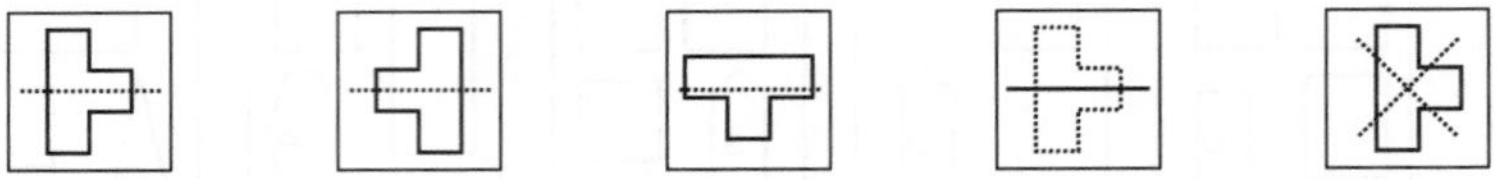

a b c d e

4.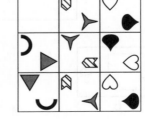

a b c d e

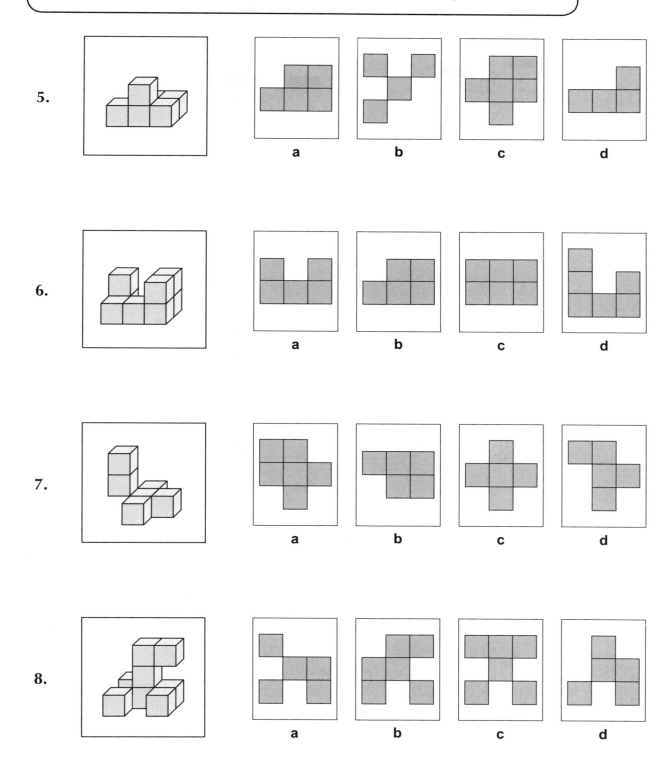

5.

a b c d

6.

a b c d

7.

a b c d

8.

a b c d

© CGP — not to be photocopied

Test 25

Work out which of the options best fits in place of the missing square in the series.

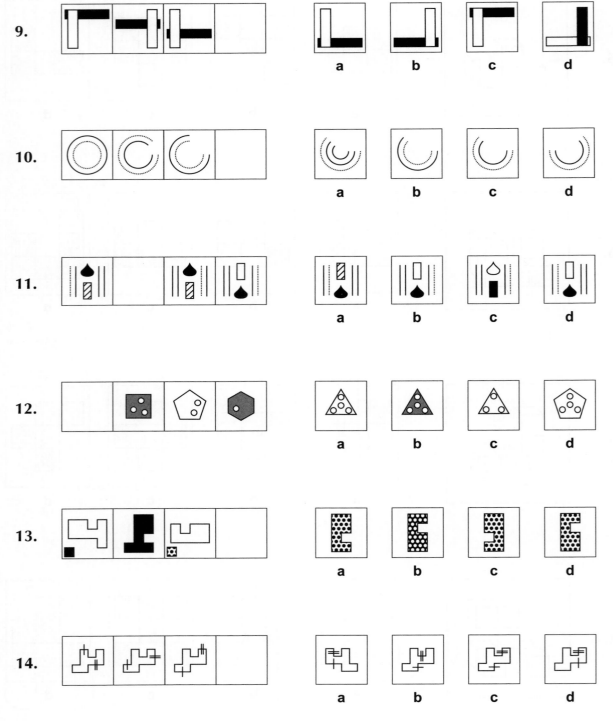

9.

     a   b   c   d

10.

     a   b   c   d

11.

     a   b   c   d

12.

     a   b   c   d

13.

     a   b   c   d

14.

     a   b   c   d

      © CGP — not to be photocopied

Work out which option would look like the figure on the left if it was reflected over the line.

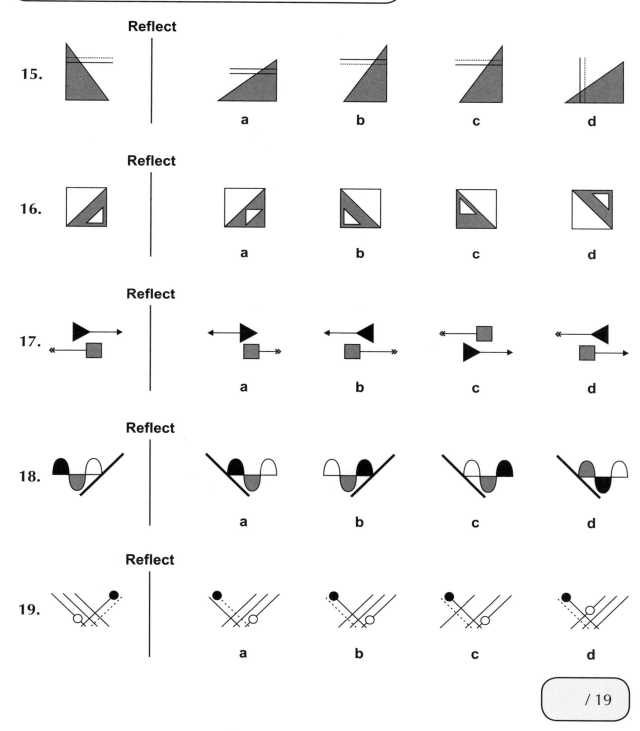

Reflect

15.

a   b   c   d

Reflect

16.

a   b   c   d

Reflect

17.

a   b   c   d

Reflect

18.

a   b   c   d

Reflect

19.

a   b   c   d

/ 19

© CGP — not to be photocopied

Test 25

Test 26

You have **10 minutes** to do this test. Circle the letter for each correct answer.

Work out which of the options best fits in place of the missing hexagon in the grid.

1.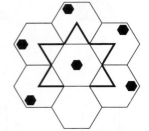

                                        a   **b**   **c**   **d**

2.

                                        a   **b**   **c**   **d**

3.

                                        a   **b**   **c**   **d**

4.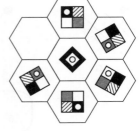

                                        a   **b**   **c**   **d**

Test 26

© CGP — not to be photocopied

Test 26

You have **10 minutes** to do this test. Circle the letter for each correct answer.

Work out which of the options best fits in place of the missing hexagon in the grid.

1.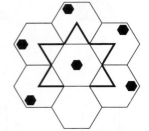

a **b** **c** **d**

2.

a **b** **c** **d**

3.

a **b** **c** **d**

4.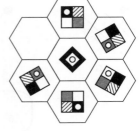

a **b** **c** **d**

Work out which option is most like the three figures on the left.

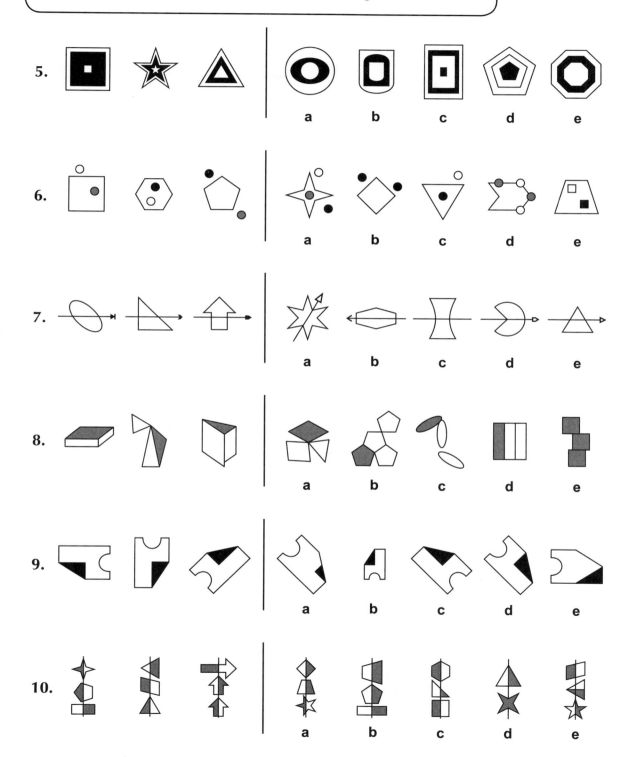

Work out which set of blocks can be put together to make the 3D figure on the left.

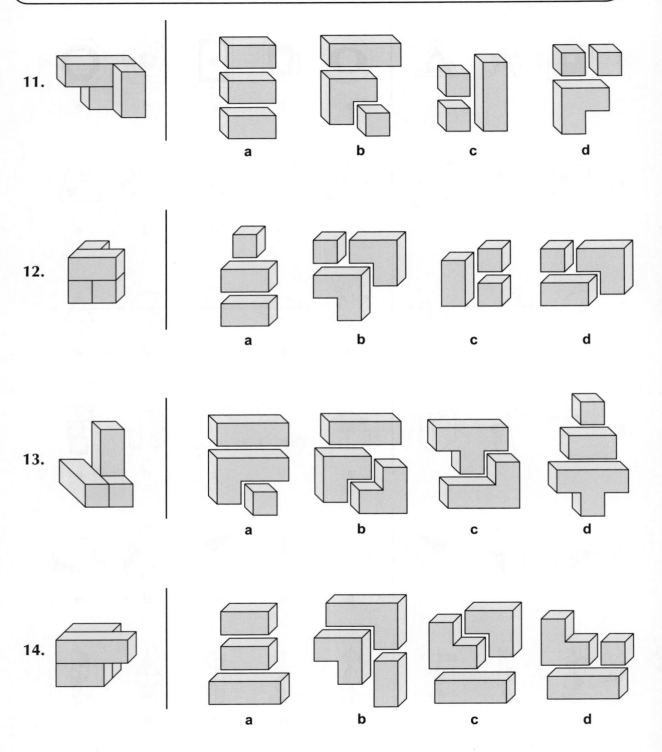

11.

a   b   c   d

12.

a   b   c   d

13.

a   b   c   d

14.

a   b   c   d

Find the figure in each row that is most unlike the others.

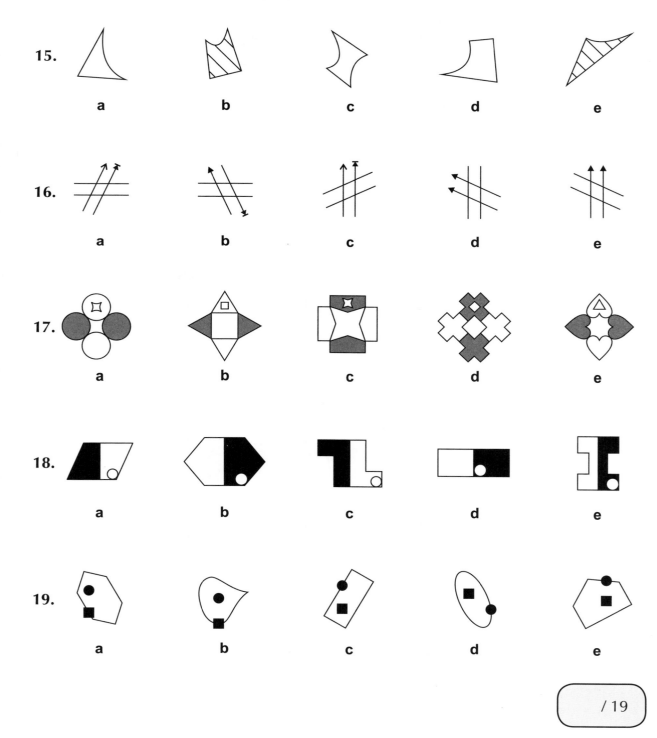

15. a   b   c   d   e

16. a   b   c   d   e

17. a   b   c   d   e

18. a   b   c   d   e

19. a   b   c   d   e

/ 19

© CGP — not to be photocopied

Test 26

You have **10 minutes** to do this test. Circle the letter for each correct answer.

Work out which option would look like the figure on the left if it was rotated.

1. **Rotate**

    a   b   c   d

2. **Rotate**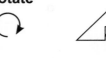

    a   b   c   d

3. **Rotate**

    a   b   c   d

4. **Rotate**

    a   b   c   d

5.   **Rotate**

    a   b   c   d

Look at how the first two figures are changed, and then work out which option would look like the third figure if you changed it in the same way.

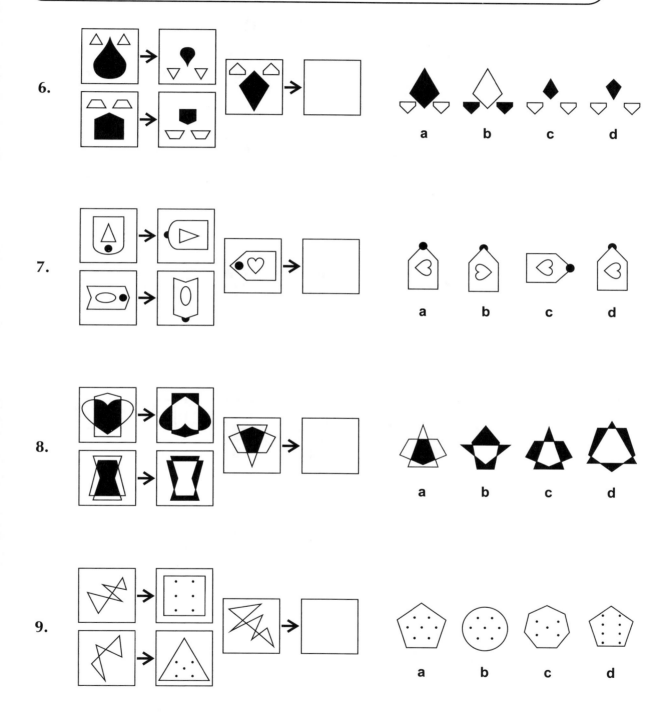

6.

7.

8.

9.

Work out which of the options best fits in place of the missing square in the series.

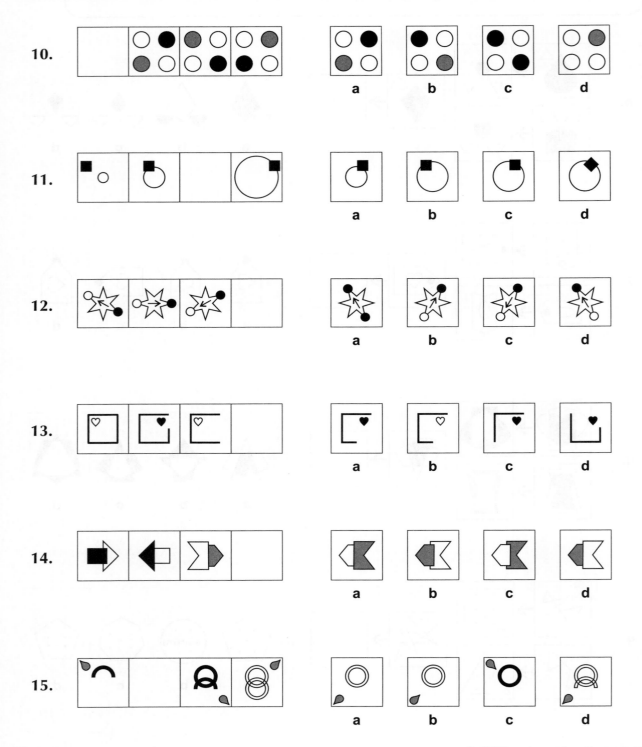

10.

a   b   c   d

11.

a   b   c   d

12.

a   b   c   d

13.

a   b   c   d

14.

a   b   c   d

15.

a   b   c   d

122

© CGP — not to be photocopied

Work out which of the four cubes can be made from the net.

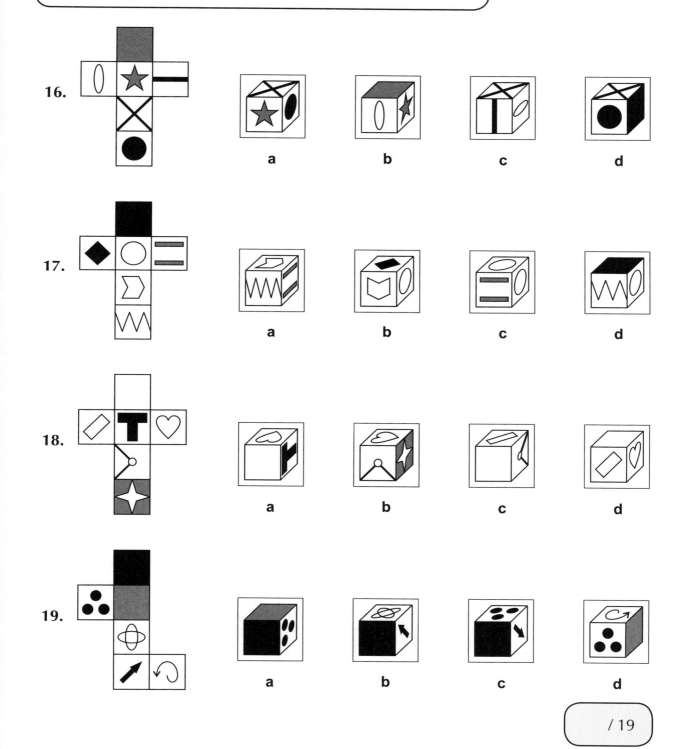

16.

a   b   c   d

17.

a   b   c   d

18.

a   b   c   d

19.

a   b   c   d

/ 19

© CGP — not to be photocopied

123

Time for a break! These puzzles are great for practising **3D shapes** and **sequencing**.

House Hunting

Match each house to the correct view from above by
writing the house number next to the correct letter.

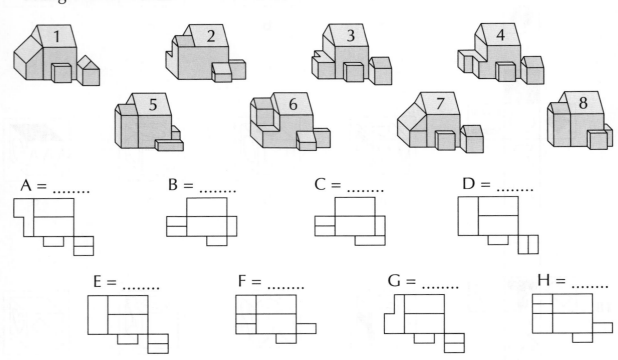

A = ...   B = ...   C = ...   D = ...

E = ...   F = ...   G = ...   H = ...

Circle Time

Put five of the figures in order by writing a number in the box underneath.
The first one has already been done for you.
One of the figures is not used in the series — put an 'X' in its box.

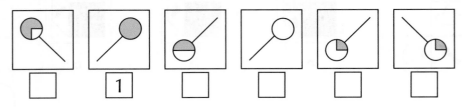

Test 28

You have **10 minutes** to do this test. Circle the letter for each correct answer.

Work out which option is most like the two figures on the left.

1.
   a   b   c   d   e

2.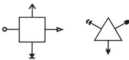
   a   b   c   d   e

3.
   a   b   c   d   e

4.
   a   b   c   d   e

5.
   a   b   c   d   e

© CGP — not to be photocopied

Work out which set of blocks can be put together to make the 3D figure on the left.

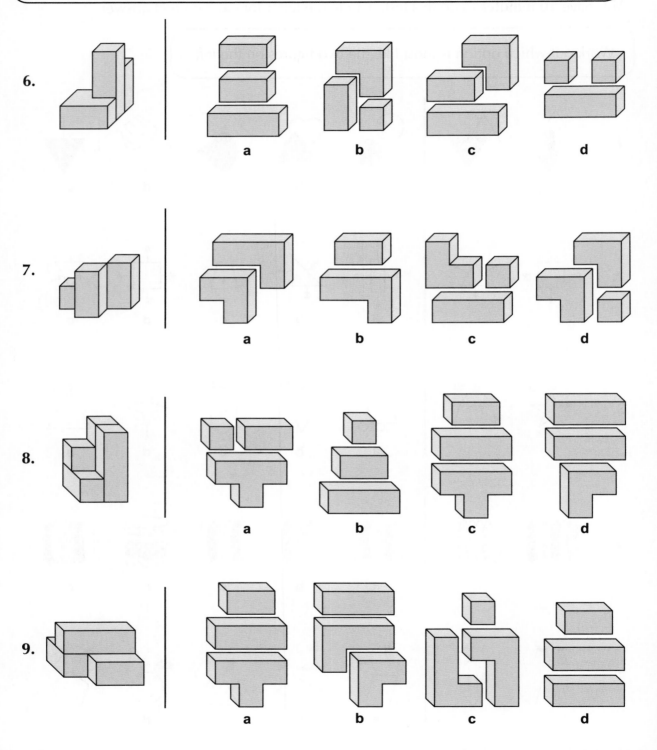

6.

a b c d

7.

a b c d

8.

a b c d

9.

a b c d

126

© CGP — not to be photocopied

Work out which of the options best fits in place of the missing square in the grid.

10.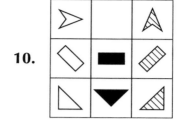

    a   b   c   d   e

11.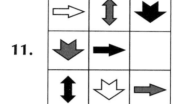

    a   b   c   d   e

12.

    a   b   c   d   e

13.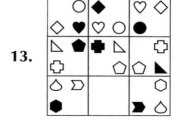

    a   b   c   d   e

© CGP — not to be photocopied

Test 28

Work out which of the options best fits in place of the missing square in the series.

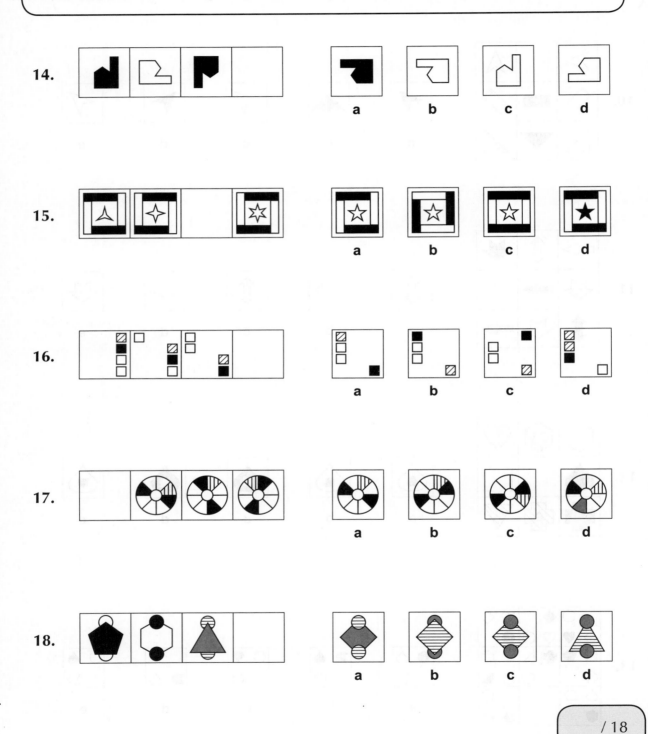

14.   a   b   c   d

15.   a   b   c   d

16.   a   b   c   d

17.   a   b   c   d

18.   a   b   c   d

/ 18

Test 29

You have **10 minutes** to do this test. Circle the letter for each correct answer.

Work out which of the options best fits in place of the missing hexagon in the grid.

1.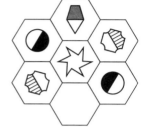

                                 a   b   c   d

2.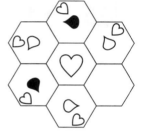

                                 a   b   c   d

3.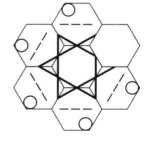

                                 a   b   c   d

4.

                               a   b   c   d

© CGP — not to be photocopied   129   Test 29

Look at how the first two figures are changed, and then work out which option would look like the third figure if you changed it in the same way.

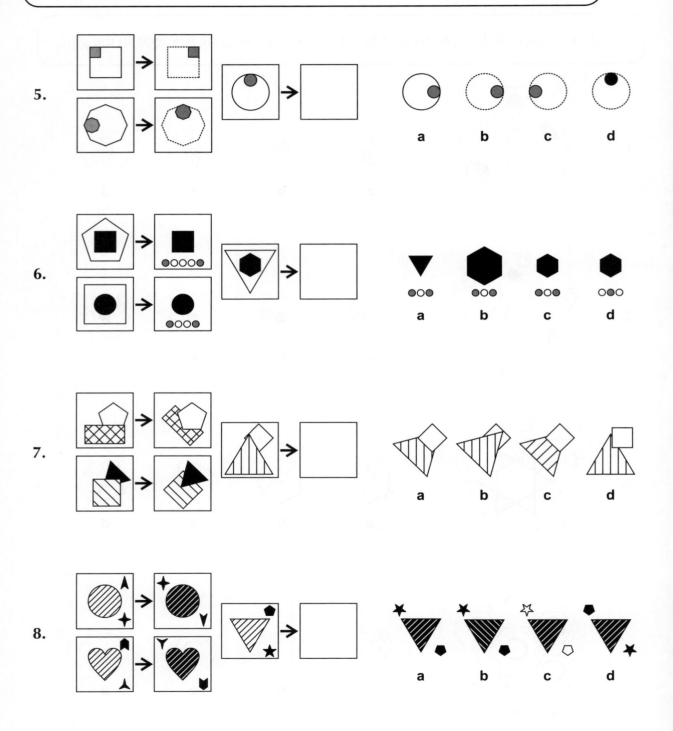

© CGP — not to be photocopied

Work out which 3D figure in the grey box has been rotated to make the new 3D figure.

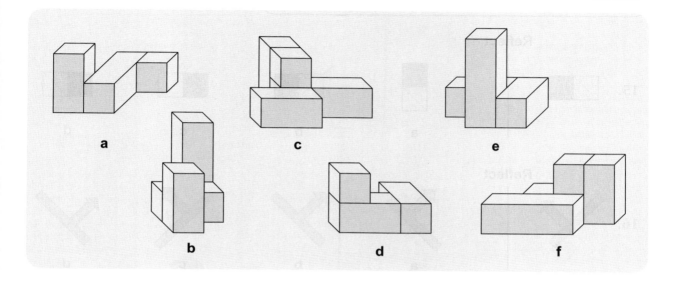

a

c

e

b

d

f

9.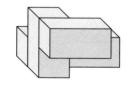

a	d
b	e
c	f

10.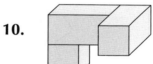

a	d
b	e
c	f

11.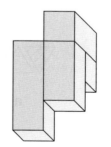

a	d
b	e
c	f

12.

a	d
b	e
c	f

13.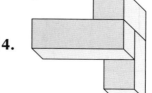

a	d
b	e
c	f

14.

a	d
b	e
c	f

© CGP — not to be photocopied

Test 29

Work out which option would look like the figure on the left if it was reflected over the line.

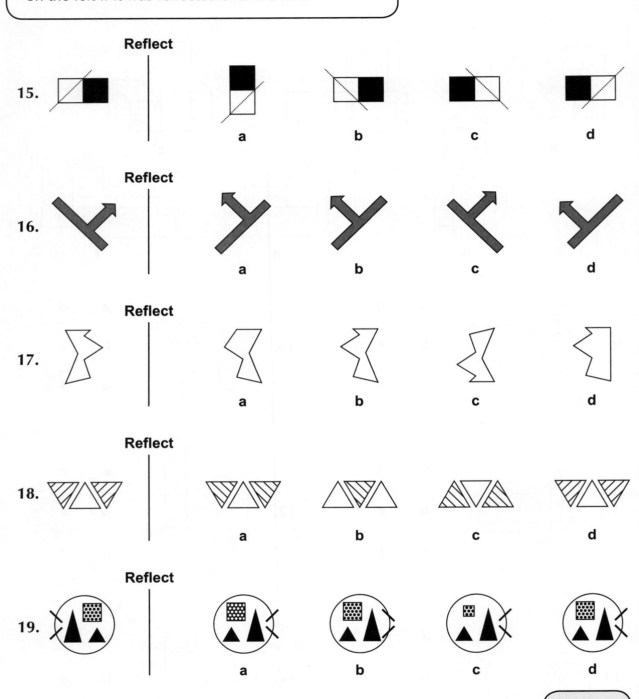

Reflect

15.

a   b   c   d

Reflect

16.

a   b   c   d

Reflect

17.

a   b   c   d

Reflect

18.

a   b   c   d

Reflect

19.

a   b   c   d

/ 19

Test 30

You have **10 minutes** to do this test. Circle the letter for each correct answer.

Work out which option would look like the figure on the left if it was rotated.

1. **Rotate**

                   a   **b**   **c**   **d**

2.  **Rotate**

                   a   **b**   **c**   **d**

3. **Rotate**

                   a   **b**   **c**   **d**

4. **Rotate**

                   a   **b**   **c**   **d**

5. **Rotate**

                   a   **b**   **c**   **d**

Find the figure in each row that is most unlike the others.

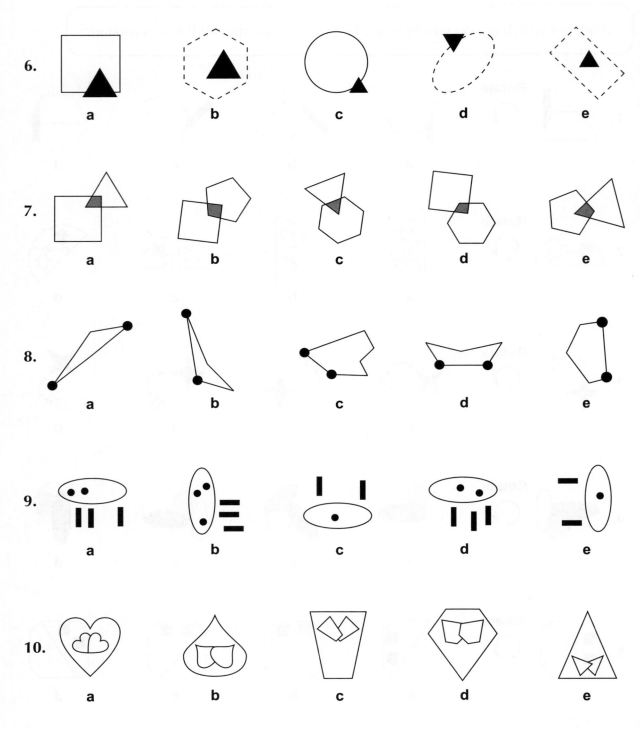

6.   a   b   c   d   e

7.   a   b   c   d   e

8.   a   b   c   d   e

9.   a   b   c   d   e

10.   a   b   c   d   e

134

© CGP — not to be photocopied

Work out which of the options best fits in place of the missing hexagon in the grid.

11.

a

b

c

d

12.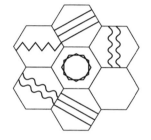

a

b

c

d

13.

a

b

c

d

14.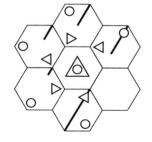

a

b

c

d

© CGP — not to be photocopied

135

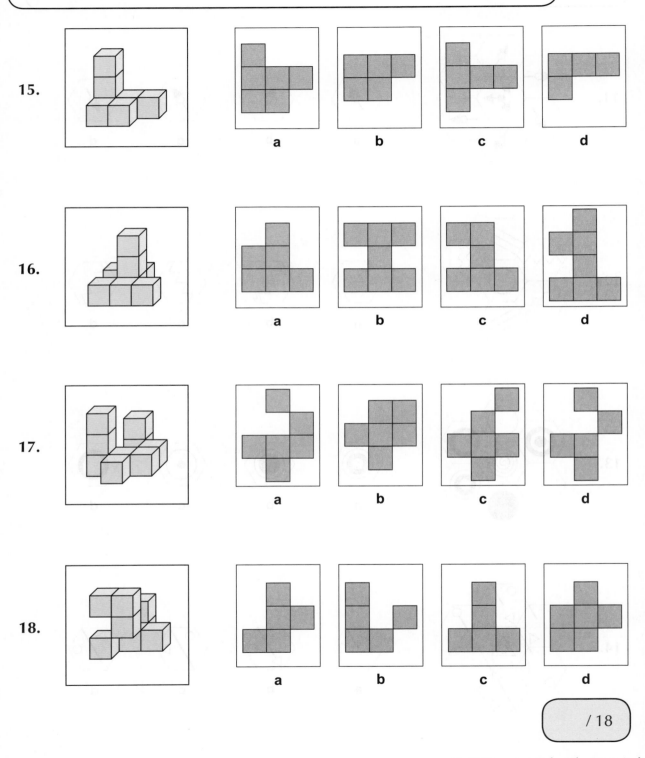

15.

a b c d

16.

a b c d

17.

a b c d

18.

a b c d

/ 18

© CGP — not to be photocopied

Test 31

You have **10 minutes** to do this test. Circle the letter for each correct answer.

Work out which option would look like the figure on the left if it was reflected over the line.

Reflect

1.

                          a   b   c   d

Reflect

2.

                          a   b   c   d

Reflect

3.

                          a   b   c   d

Reflect

4.

                          a   b   c   d

Reflect

5.

                          a   b   c   d

© CGP — not to be photocopied

Look at how the first bug changes to become the second bug. Then work out which option would look like the third bug if you changed it in the same way.

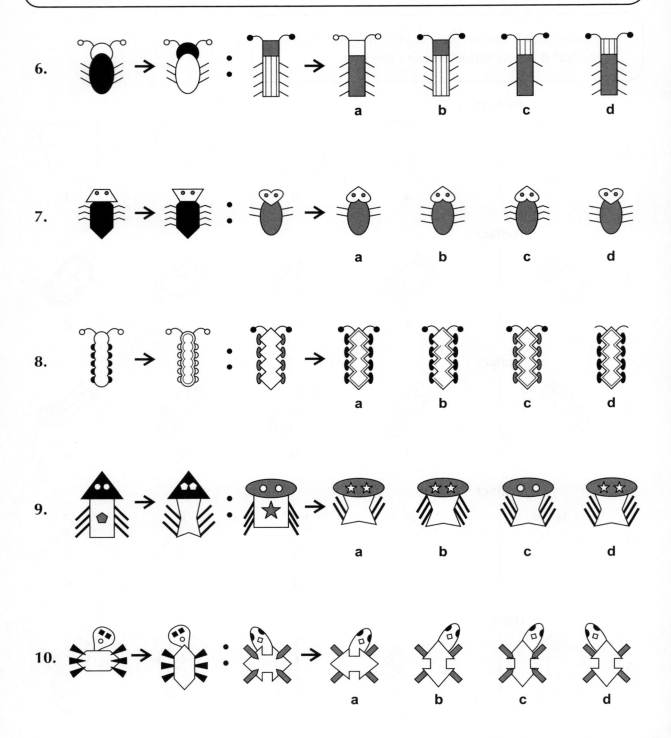

6.

a b c d

7.

a b c d

8.

a b c d

9.

a b c d

10.

a b c d

138

© CGP — not to be photocopied

Work out which of the four cubes can be made from the net.

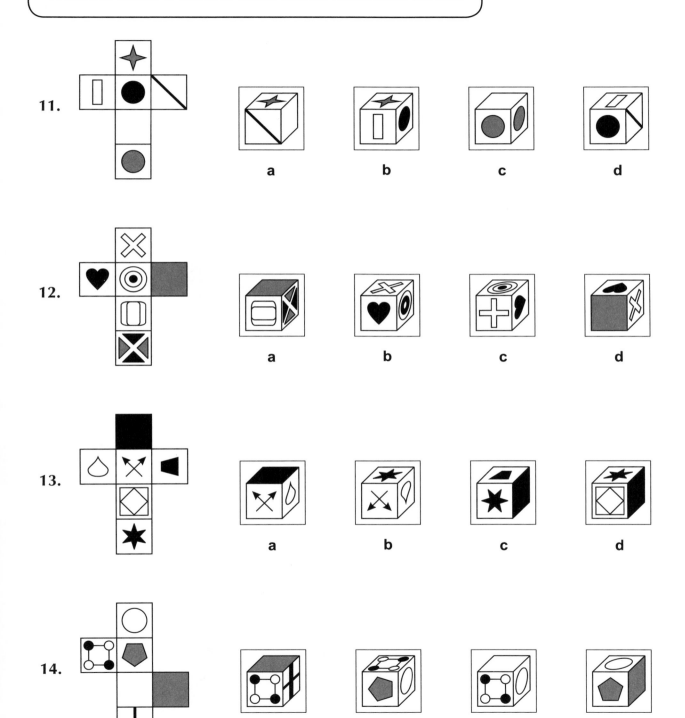

11.   a   b   c   d

12.   a   b   c   d

13.   a   b   c   d

14.   a   b   c   d

© CGP — not to be photocopied   139

Work out which of the options best fits in place of the missing hexagon in the grid.

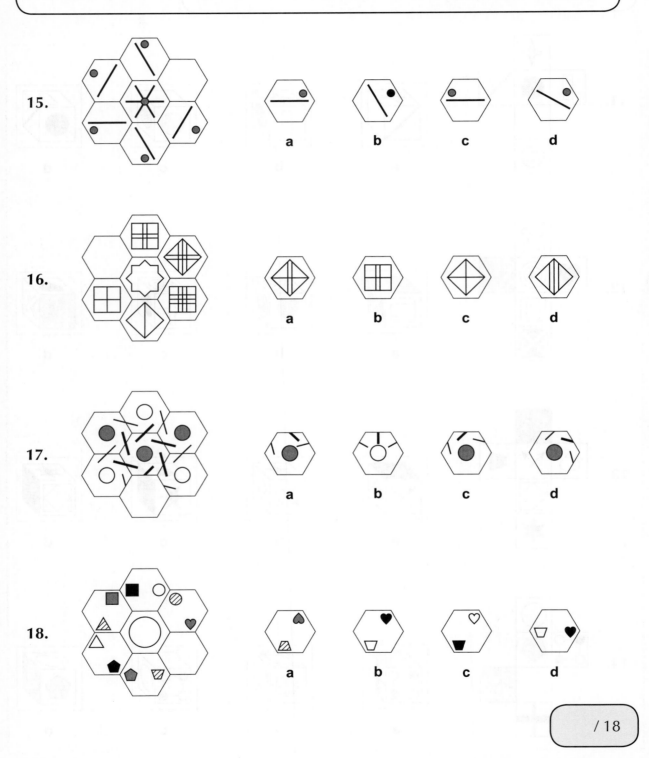

15.

a   b   c   d

16.

a   b   c   d

17.

a   b   c   d

18.

a   b   c   d

/ 18

Try these puzzles — they're a great way to practise spotting how things are **linked**.

Robot Replacement

Robot A can be changed into Robot B in 7 steps. Only one feature changes in each step. Write the numbers in the boxes to put the steps in order.

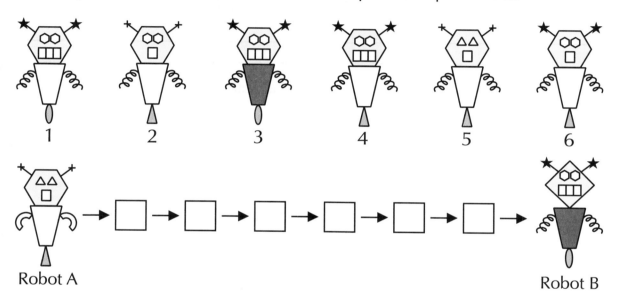

Drawing Nets

Four identical cubes are arranged below. Complete the net of the cubes.

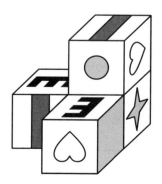
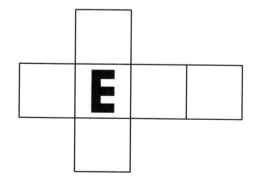

© CGP — not to be photocopied

Puzzles 10

Glossary

Rotation and Reflection

Rotation is when a shape is turned clockwise or anticlockwise from its starting point.

Example shape

90 degree clockwise rotation

45 degree anticlockwise rotation

180 degree rotation

Reflection is when something is mirrored over an imaginary line.

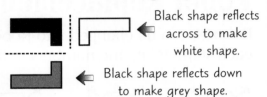

Black shape reflects across to make white shape.

Black shape reflects down to make grey shape.

3D Rotation

There are **three planes** that a 3D shape can be rotated in.

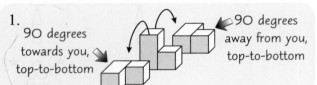

1. 90 degrees towards you, top-to-bottom

90 degrees away from you, top-to-bottom

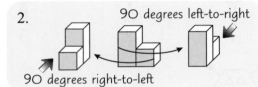

2. 90 degrees left-to-right

90 degrees right-to-left

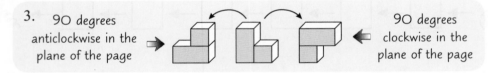

3. 90 degrees anticlockwise in the plane of the page

90 degrees clockwise in the plane of the page

Other Terms

Figure — the picture as a whole that makes up one example or option in a question.

Arrow-style Line — a line with a small shape at one end.

Line Types:

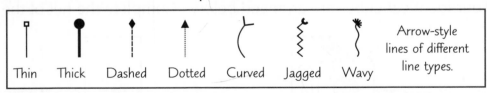

Thin   Thick   Dashed   Dotted   Curved   Jagged   Wavy

Arrow-style lines of different line types.

Shading Types:

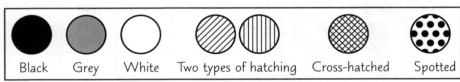

Black   Grey   White   Two types of hatching   Cross-hatched   Spotted

Layering — when a shape is in front of or behind other shapes.

Line of Symmetry — a line which splits a shape into halves that are reflections of each other.

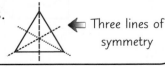
Three lines of symmetry

© CGP — not to be photocopied

N6XPDE1